1

Mangia

Sara Garofalo

EPH

To Italy

CONTENTS

FOREWORD

In this fast-paced world, where achievement and success often dominate our lives, it's easy to lose sight of what truly matters—our connection to ourselves, our bodies, and our souls. We become trapped in a relentless cycle of striving, pushing ourselves to the limit, and neglecting the very essence of who we are. But it doesn't have to be this way.

Within the pages of this remarkable cookbook, Mangia, Sara invites us on a transformative journey, one that bridges the gap between the Italian and Indian cultures, offering us a path to heal our relationship with ourselves and find true fulfillment.

Sara shares her own vulnerable story—facing her own demons, battling eating disorders and experiencing periods of self-doubt. But through the profound wisdom found in the traditions of both Italian and Indian cultures, she has not only healed herself but also discovered a powerful message of hope and transformation. Her passion for helping others, particularly stressed-out, type A, workaholic women, is evident in every page of this book.

As a fellow type A overachiever who once believed that success could be found solely in external achievements, I can personally attest to the transformative power of Sara's teachings. Through her compassionate guidance and deep understanding of the human experience, Sara has unlocked the secret to reconnecting with our spirits, rekindling our relationship with our bodies, and embracing a life of pleasure and happiness. Mangia is not just a cookbook; it's a roadmap to self-discovery and Healing.

Paden Hughes, Author & Speaker

Sara's book, Mangia is a reflection of the life she embodies: pleasure, love, compassion, grace, determination and radical honesty. She boldly lives in a way that nurtures and uplifts everything she comes into contact with. She has shown me how pleasurable and rejuvenating food can be through her recipes as well as how much fun and effortless cooking for my family can be while truly savoring every taste on my palette.

Minh Truong, LCSW

INTRODUCTION

"Mangia", the word that has permeated the walls of my home since I can remember.

"Mangia" means "Eat".

As I write this word, I can picture my dad sitting at the head of the table saying it in his loud Italian voice while pointing at the plate in front of me with a typical Italian hand gesture. Next, he would grab a piece of fresh bread and say "To, mangia", meaning "here you go, eat". After that he would grab a piece of cheese and say "mangia." I could sit here for hours painting these little moments that colored my Italian upbringing but to make a long story short, I would hear the word "Mangia" at least ten times per day. If it wasn't my dad saying this, it was my mom, or grandma, or grandpa, or brother, or uncle or auntie...I have a big Italian family that has lived in the same area for generations and generations. So, you get the picture, right?

I decided to write this health cookbook for a few reasons. First of all, this book is an act of gratitude toward my family and my culture. I wouldn't be who I am today if my mom didn't raise me on home-cooked, freshly made meals...for every meal. My mom would make the perfect amount that needed to be finished at each meal. The only leftovers I ate for the first eighteen years of my life were homemade pizza and leftovers after birthday parties, Easter and Christmas. Other than that, leftovers were not allowed.

She cooked everything from scratch every day from the moment I was born. She takes a lot of pride in never giving me the premade baby food in jars. Instead, she would make it fresh every day.

Yes, I was spoiled with food—to the point that I couldn't really eat anything else but my mom's food for years! But I love food. Food is a big part of who I am and I want to share it with you.

Another reason why I am writing this health cookbook is to honor my studies around Ayurveda and how it changed the trajectory of my life. It is, in fact, one of the most ancient holistic healing sciences on Earth that originated in India more than 5,000 years ago. Ayurveda transformed my way of living, thinking, and understanding the medicinal and energetic properties of foods, herbs, and spices. I have a whole chapter about this that you can look forward to.

I am also writing this health cookbook to offer you a different approach to traditional weight loss strategies by being more intentional about what and how you eat. It is my intention to give you a roadmap by taking a spiritual weight loss approach and show you that you can heal yourself, access your body's wisdom, and develop your inner compass (aka your intuition around food).

It is my honor and duty to be of service, to activate people and raise consciousness.

Let the journey begin.

Light and Love,

Sara

My Food
JOURNEY

The
BEGINNING

Flashback to 2009: I was staring in the mirror and did not recognize my own reflection. Puffy face, puffy eyes, inflamed, out-of-shape, and having a hard time fitting into my clothes. I felt lost, misunderstood, angry and lonely. I had gained weight and hated the look and feel of being in my own body. I was sixteen years old. All I wanted was to be accepted, loved, comfortable, and at peace with myself. But that was not my reality.

I remember the worried look on my parents' faces, discussing the possibility of seeking professional help. I felt ashamed for what I was doing to myself, but I could not stop it. I didn't know how.

I refused to eat normal food, instead, I would snack on unhealthy foods in my bedroom or late at night when no one could see me. To my parents, it looked like I wasn't eating, but, in reality, all of my calories were being consumed in secret. I thought I could lose weight by myself, but the more I tried sticking to a diet and not eating, the more my binging intensified.

Then the vomiting started. I would run to the bathroom after binging on all the sweet snacks and foods in the cupboard and induce retching (and pain) by sticking my fingers deep down into my throat until something came up. I did this for a few months until my throat hurt so badly that I was traumatized and just couldn't do it anymore. I felt like my only option for losing weight, while still being able to binge, was gone in a heartbeat.

Depression followed. My mental health declined rapidly. I did not want to socialize with friends and couldn't play any sports due to a hip injury. All I did was spend time in my room and study. Well, at least something good came out of that dark period of my life: I was an A+ student, although inside, I was failing.

One year later, I was sitting in the white, cold waiting room of a dietitian my mom chose to send me to. Dr. T. came out and called my name; she was as skinny as a "grissino" (the Italian breadstick) with wrinkles all over her face and arms. She wore a tight dress and high heels. Her energy was as cold as ice.

"Am I seeing some far-away cousin of Cruella de Vil? She does not look healthy to me", I thought to myself.

She asked me to get on the scales and weigh myself.

My heart pounded inside of my chest like a rullo di tamburi (drum roll).

"Is there a back door where I can escape?" I asked myself while looking at every corner of that cold, white room.

I took my shoes and clothes off and stepped on the scale. I did not look. Dr. T. said "63 Kg," equivalent to 139 pounds. Then she grabbed the measuring tape and measured my bloated belly, arms and thighs.

I wanted to die.

She handed me my diet and gave my mom the directions since she was going to be cooking for me.

"I will see you in one month," Dr. T. said.

"Oh, crap," I thought to myself, getting into the boxy, yellow car my mom drove at the time.

My 1200-calorie restrictive diet officially began. Something else began that I had not considered before that moment: my obsession with calorie counting and tracking.

Under a very strict regimen that did not allow any fun foods like sweets or treats, my mom and I weighed everything. I could not eat out, go to a social event or enjoy anything that was not in one of the 20 pages of Dr. T.'s plan.

I was determined. I often pride myself on being committed to and achieving my goals, but this did not serve my greatest purpose in that particular situation. Instead, it took me down a path of control, restriction, deprivation, obsession, and further away from loving myself and my body.

I was literally "hating my body into being thin." Worst of all, I damaged my mental health. And my relationship with food was spiraling even further down a path of aggressive control.

REACHING *my* WEIGHT ∞

2010. The day had come. I was back at Dr. T.'s office for the 9th month. I had lost all the extra weight and I saw the number I had been working toward: "52 Kg or 114.5 pounds." I had finally made it.

But that was not real happiness. An obsession for more, haunted me. I wasn't satisfied or happy with myself nor did I know how to live without being on a diet.

I remained anxious, lost, and scared, but I was at the other end of the spectrum foodwise. I was no longer suffering from binge eating, instead, I had gained control—too much control—and now I didn't know how to live a normal life. I developed a detailed plan for fake eating during social events. My appearance became more important than anything else. My Ego had grown bigger and taller. I was finally the girl everyone wanted to see, at least from a physical perspective.

Inside I was still broken, and most importantly, the self-love I hoped to achieve had been washed away by wanting to look good in my old clothes—at any given cost.

Searching for
ANSWERS ⤬

At eighteen years old, I was tired of being trapped in the prison I had created. Calorie counting/ tracking, obsessive workouts, anxiety while attending social events, and never feeling good in my own body affected my relationship with myself and everyone else in my life.

I needed to figure out who I was and deeply connect with myself. I felt that I had become what society wanted me to be, but I had no idea who I wanted to be. I didn't recognize who I even was at this point. On the outside, I was a grade A student, a black belt in Karate, a guitar player, and I had a great community. However, I felt no one understood my pain or the agony I was experiencing inside.

There must be another way, I thought.

I left home on my first soul-searching adventure: "wwoofing" for three months in the US.

WWOOF, World Wide Opportunities on Organic Farms, is a program that gives people the opportunity to volunteer on a variety of organic properties. I helped on the land and in the home for 4-6 hours a day; my hosts provided food and accommodation. I needed to go back to the basics: just me and nature.

When that chapter ended, I went back home to Italy for two weeks and then left for Australia. I had my Visa, an au pair job, and a plane ticket. I was following "the call".

I worked as an au pair in Australia for about 2.5 months before I left for an ashram, a spiritual retreat center, near Byron Bay. (Funnily enough, the owner of that ashram was from the same Italian village where I went to high school, 10 minutes away from where my parents now live. The Universe!)

It was here that I experienced my first (food) spiritual awakening journey.

DISCOVERING MY LIFE *Purpose*

During my time at the ashram, I met a fifty-year-old woman that I felt very magnetized to in some ways. Barefoot, with long linen trousers, a linen shirt, and a beautiful Indian shawl. She had reddish wavy hair, and bright green eyes and appeared awakened for her age. She gave a workshop about Ayurveda. At the time, I knew nothing about Ayurveda but immediately found it fascinating enough to want to study it. I wanted to give myself some time to integrate and digest everything I had learned from the workshop, so instead of diving right into it again, I decided to keep traveling and put some energy into enhancing my intuitive gifts as a clairvoyant and energy healer (but that's a story for another time). I traveled to Thailand and then New Zealand and found myself working on a 700-acre cattle farm, where I was building fences, baling hay, and maintaining both farm equipment and facilities. I took care of 100 young heifers, monitored the herd for signs of illness and/or injuries, and took charge of making three meals a day for three people every day: the owner, my boyfriend at the time, and me. I became overwhelmed by the demands and stress of my daily activities. As a result, I started eating more comfort foods with high amounts of carbs and sugar, gained 10 Kg (22 lb) in less than three months, and developed a yeast infection because my diet accompanied by the stress created imbalances in my microflora. After all of those intense years of hard-core dieting, I was spiraling, feeling disappointed and frustrated, I felt like I was going back to square one.

I packed my bags and went back home. And after a strict candida protocol, I decided to enroll in a program to become an Ayurvedic Counselor. I was ready to be done with the toxic cycle, so I committed to my health journey. I was very excited to learn about this ancient holistic science that was focused on the mind-body connection and the root cause of disease.

I am not going to lie about the fact that, in the beginning, I had a love-hate relationship with Ayurveda. It was interesting, mind-blowing, and so darn complicated at the same time! I had to take a break for quite a few months after my certification program because I was overwhelmed by the amount of information that I had received in a short amount of time. I took my time to process and apply the knowledge. I created my daily routine, practiced listening to my body, adjusted my dietary needs according to my mind-body constitution, and connected with myself every day.

Learning about Ayurveda was like remembering my body's language. It ended up being the key to healing my relationship with food and becoming intuitive about my body, a gift that I now have the honor to share with others.

In my work as a Spiritual Weight Loss Coach, I apply what I learned from Ayurveda to help women find food freedom, heal their relationship with food, and help them navigate their spiritual awakening journey.

I love helping women heal their relationships with their bodies and themselves by blending Ayurvedic practices with RIM (Regenerating Images in Memory) and my intuitive gifts. I use Ayurveda to help women get in touch with their own mind-body constitution. I use RIM (Regenerating Images in Memory) Essentials to help my clients subconsciously reprogram their brains. And I use my intuitive gifts to aid my ability to identify and free blockages in my client's bodies and allow them to heal. Helping people transform their lives from the inside out in these ways is my dharma, otherwise known as my soul's purpose.

I truly believe that part of my life's purpose is to help spread Ayurvedic knowledge by simplifying it for people so they can understand this amazing deep ancient healing science and use it to heal their body, mind, and soul. I believe I am meant to be the bridge for people from the unconscious to the conscious world.

THE DIFFERENCE BETWEEN DIET
and lifestyle

The biggest difference between the two is that dieting is a short-term process while lifestyle change is long-term.

No matter what you choose, it is important that you understand the difference.

Dieting focuses on restricting calories, counting, weighing, tracking, depriving the body of certain nutrients, and excessively working out because you want to lose weight fast. When you choose this route, I invite you to think of the energy required to succeed.

Dieting can be a very controlling, masculine way of reaching a goal. You are choosing to reach your goal(s) no matter the cost, even when the cost is your mental health and your relationship with food. Dieting forces you to micromanage and control every aspect of your life in order to achieve the results you want. However, your body hates forced restrictions. These restrictions activate your fight or flight response as a form of

protection, leading you to gain most of the weight, if not more, back. Keeping you stuck in the cycle.

A lifestyle change is more focused on a long-term solution to reaching the same goals but in a very different way. Again, I invite you to look at the energy you're going to need to expend for this choice. It is not just about what you eat—it's a commitment to bettering yourself as a whole. Your goals may range anywhere from diet, exercise, reading, and goal setting to meditation. These changes will be unique for everyone because everyone's reason for wanting a lifestyle change is different. In all cases, however, these changes are absolutely beneficial for the longevity of life as they may ease daily stress.

The most important part of a lifestyle change is that there is purpose behind it. If there is no purpose to ground yourself in, the chances of you giving up when life gets hard increase. Having your "why" serves as a healthy reminder to keep you motivated with a positive mental attitude.

Along with a set purpose, it is also helpful to have a support group to be there along the way. This can be a friend, a family member, a coach, or even an online/local group. Whatever works for you.

If dieting is a masculine approach to weight loss, making a lifestyle change would be the more feminine approach to weight loss and it includes intuitive eating as a step to creating lasting change. When you switch from dieting to intuitive eating, you are making a very important choice: you are deciding to switch from forcing your body into being healthy to listening to your body's intuition and guidance.

The feminine approach is a softer energy that consists of flowing instead of pushing. It's the moon energy and is all about listening to the body's clues to whether you are having a physical response (i.g. hunger pangs) or an emotional response (sadness, anxiety, etc.). When you take this approach, rather than relying on external factors to determine how much you eat and move, you turn inwards and listen to your own body. The feminine energy is all about trust and respect towards your feelings and emotions.

What is INTUITIVE EATING

Intuitive eating is a philosophy of eating that makes you the expert of your body and its hunger signals. Essentially, it's the opposite of a traditional diet. It doesn't impose guidelines about what to avoid and what or when to eat. Instead, it teaches that you are the best person–the only person–to make those choices. The term was coined in 1995 by two dietitians, Elyse Resche and Evelyn Tribole, and it includes 10 principles:

- Reject the Diet Mentality
- Honor Your Hunger
- Make Peace with Food
- Challenge the Food Police
- Discover the Satisfaction Factor
- Feel Your Fullness
- Cope with Your Emotions with Kindness
- Respect Your Body
- Movement—Feel the Difference
- Honor Your Health—Gentle Nutrition

So how can you start to take a feminine approach to weight loss that will produce lasting results? Here are five major shifts to make to ditch the diet and become a more intuitive eater:

#1 Ditch Counting Calories

When you stop counting every calorie you consume, you will notice a great sense of emotional lightness. You will receive immediate energy from this. You don't need to continue to feel anxious about hitting a calorie count all the time.

#2 Ditch the Scale

When you constantly weigh yourself, you create an obsession. Instead, tune into how you feel. Do you feel good, bloated, energized, or tired today? Stop relying on a number to validate how good you feel.

#3 Learn your Mind-Body Constitution

Discovering my mind-body constitution, according to the ancient wisdom of Ayurveda, allows you to free yourself from the myth of "caloric deficit" vs "digestive health." As long as your digestive system runs appropriately, you are healthy and you will return to your natural body weight effortlessly.

#4 Practice Listening to Your Hunger Cues

After years of dieting, it's essential to re-establish a connection with your hunger cues. You've been conditioned to disconnect from your natural body cues for so long, so it's a muscle you will need to retrain. It takes time, but you will get there.

#5 Needs vs. Wants

Asking yourself what you crave and want vs what you should eat today is a crucial step in ditching the masculine approach of dieting. When we practice the feminine approach to weight loss, it isn't about what you should eat, but what you feel like eating. Every day will be different. You are NOT a robot. Reaching a healthy weight and a positive body image should not feel like a struggle. If you feel like you are struggling, re-evaluate your approach.

So now that you've learned the difference between dieting and intuitive eating, I'd like to introduce you to the concept of taking a "holistic" approach, if you are not already familiar with it.

Even though these steps are insightful and helpful, I didn't achieve intuitive eating by reading a book; I achieved it through Ayurveda.

When I started eating for my dosha or my mind-body constitution, I was able to connect with my inner nature, balance my body and emotional well-being, and become whole. Understanding your mind-body constitution allows you to understand how and why food impacts your body functions, gut health, and emotional state.

The food you eat can impact your mental health. I will give you an example. Rosie was having consistent anxiety as well as bloating and constipation. She thought it was normal to be constipated and she didn't know how to balance her anxiety. When I asked her what she was eating, she mentioned salads every night and a smoothie every day. Immediately this caught my attention. According to Ayurveda, the food you eat has a specific energy determined by one of the natural elements: fire, water, space, earth, and air. Salads and smoothies are raw foods. Raw foods, in Ayurvedic practices, are primarily made out of air energy.

An individual with anxiety has too much air in her/his body, which translates into the physical in the form of gas, bloating, constipation (in the physical body), and anxiety (in the emotional body).

Ayurveda teaches that "like increases like". So if Rosie already has too much air, she should stay away from foods that cause more air in her body. She should balance it with the opposite–earth-quality foods. Once Rosie started avoiding cold, raw foods and introducing cooked, warm, grounding foods into her body, her constipation was alleviated, and she started to notice an improvement in her anxiety level. She was eating more intuitively, and it made all the difference.

So how does an Intuitive eater eat? Intuitive eaters pick their foods based on internal signals like hunger, fullness, satisfaction, and body respect rather than external cues like food rules, restrictions, or the whims of Instagram followers. Intuitive eaters give themselves permission to eat whatever they want without any food guilt. They trust their bodies to tell them when, what, and how much to eat. They can tell when they feel like eating vegetables and when they want to have dessert. And they don't judge themselves for either decision. The best part of Ayurveda is that it teaches you the skills to eat intuitively according to your mind-body type and enables you to live a balanced life.

The Itaveda
APPROACH

BLENDING MY ITALIAN ROOTS
with Ayurveda

I created my own term "ITAVEDA" by blending my Italian roots with Ayurveda.

What makes the ITAVEDA approach unique?

The ITAVEDA approach blends together two of the most ancient cultures in history, Italian and Ayurveda. Italian culture revolves around food. Growing up in Italy, we would come together to share a meal, talk, and enjoy delicious foods together. For Italians, food is life, family, and community. Ayurveda, or the "science of life," taught me to look at food from a medicinal point of view. I learned the energies and the different tastes of the foods. I learned to adjust my plate to balance my mental health and/or gut health. I learned that foods affect your mental health and vice-versa. It taught me the holistic and energetic way of looking at food from a mind-body-soul perspective. Ayurveda taught me to look for the root cause of the disease.

I've taken the best from both of these worlds and blended them into a practice. Here are some of the values I've adopted from each culture.

SIMILARITIES

#1 Three Consistent Meals A Day

In my experience, Italians are creatures of habit. Over the course of centuries, both Italians and Indians have figured out some important rituals and habits to stay healthy. Habits create structure and a rhythm for the body to feel safe. If you want to get out of fight or flight and regulate your metabolism quickly, start having three consistent meals a day.

Consistency is one of the most important strategies in maintaining a healthy weight. According to Ayurveda, having three meals a day helps to regulate our metabolism. When we don't eat for long periods of time, we end up activating a "stress" response.

For example, I often hear my clients say that they wake up, drink coffee and maybe have breakfast on the go, and due to their busy schedule, they don't eat again until dinner. At around 5 pm they are starving, drinking wine and snacking while cooking, followed by a huge dinner that they can't metabolize before bedtime. When they go to bed, it is hard for them to sleep well because their stomach is still too full.

A better strategy is to try having lunch and a lighter dinner and see what happens! Usually, my clients find amazing improvements almost immediately in their energy levels and sleep quality.

#2 The Art of Eating Consciously

The second commonality Italians and Ayurveda share is the Art of Eating Consciously. The time to sit and enjoy a meal in peace. Carving time to enjoy your meal brings mindfulness to the act of eating and it will help digest the food well. Take a look at the environment where you eat your food. Is it a calm and peaceful place? Often it's not. Many people eat on the run, sometimes not even taking the time to sit down, much less care about the environment. Oftentimes, people eat in cluttered dining areas, noisy cafeterias under bright fluorescent lights, in the car on the way to work, or while engaged in conflict or debate. These environments make it nearly impossible to focus on the foods we are eating and how our body feels as it receives the food.

When the environment is cluttered or active, the mind becomes cluttered and active making it difficult to focus. Agitation and distraction make it very difficult to control your eating habits. So for your next meal, create a space you can relax into and carve out some time to really enjoy and pay attention to the food you're eating.

#3 Whole Fresh Ingredients

The third similarity between the two cultures is the consumption of whole, seasonal, fresh foods (there's a reason Italian food tastes better in Italy). Rather than the food itself, it's really Prana—life force energy—that nourishes the body at the most fundamental level and is responsible for the creation of health, vitality, and energy. This category includes fresh, whole, minimally processed, locally grown and organic foods.

#4 Cooking Your Own Meals

In Ayurveda & in Italian culture, it is believed that the energy, attitude, intention and feelings you have while cooking are infused into the food. This energy is then absorbed and digested into the person receiving it. So cooking with love, devotion, and kind energy is essential for optimal digestion.

I typically make most meals at home instead of eating out. I could sit here and make the argument about how much money you would save, but my point is different. I look through the lens of health. Salad dressings, salsas, and restaurant foods are naturally heavier, saltier, more sugary, and in my opinion, overly seasoned than what you would normally make for yourself at home. When you eat out every day it's not good for your health because most restaurant meals are higher in salt, sugar, and fat, and how the food was prepared is frequently unknown. Also according to Italians, if you start using high-quality organic ingredients, the food tastes amazing by itself!

#5 Eat Your Largest Meal Of The Day At Lunchtime

Ayurveda says that the digestive Agni (digestive fire, the Ayurvedic term for the strength and volume of stomach acid, digestive enzymes, and bile in the GI tract) is maximum during lunchtime. Your body is wired according to the movement of the sun and your digestive agni is naturally high when the sun is the strongest. Therefore, as the sun goes down, you should also gradually reduce your heavy food intake. Interestingly enough, Italians value lunchtime more than dinner time in terms of the heaviness/lightness of the meal.

#6 Snacking

If you cruise through any typical American grocery store, you will no doubt find aisle upon aisle of various snacks and treats. Chips, cookies, granola bars, crackers, basically anything sweet, salty, and crunchy seems to constitute a good stand-in for a meal. But, is a diet consisting of a small breakfast, a snack, lunch, snack, dinner, followed by another snack a sensible way to eat? According to Ayurveda, the answer is simple: no.

Italians agree with Ayurveda, that there is no such thing as a snack. They believe in a strong meal, with antipasto (appetizer), primo (first course), secondo (second course), and dolce (dessert).

#7 Pleasure

What is the most important ingredient in eating? Pleasure. Both Italians and Ayurveda agree on this topic. You can add all of the medicinal ingredients you want, but if you don't enjoy the taste, it's not Ayurvedic. A balanced meal is designed to lead to physical and emotional enjoyment.

DIFFERENCES

#1 Simplicity

One of the major differences between the two cultures is the contrast between the simplicity of Italian recipes versus the complexity of Ayurvedic recipes. Most culinary experts agree that Italian cooking is mainly about simple recipes, quality ingredients, cooking techniques, and passion. On the other hand, Ayurveda teaches that we need to eat a balance of six basic flavors to be well-nourished and emotionally content. Ayurvedic recipes combine many herbs and spices into one meal. Most of the time I prefer to keep the simplicity of taste in my recipes, therefore adopting the Italian way of making meals with occasional Ayurvedic recipes.

#2 Alcohol

The consumption of alcohol is a major cultural difference. In Italy, we have aperitivo, which means cocktail in Italian. Between 5:30-7pm,

people head to the nearest bar and have drinks and light snacks to whet their appetite. People don't do this on a regular basis. But when they do, it is usually because it is a way of socializing with coworkers and/or friends at the end of the day, or they are celebrating something special and visiting with friends or family. Aperitivi might include Aperol spritz drinks with little bites.

On the other hand, Ayurveda believes that alcohol quickly and directly impacts the heart and mind, influencing the doshas. The ultimate result is that alcohol detracts from our ojas, or the subtle life force in our body that determines our mental and physical radiance. Over time, regular alcohol consumption thus leads to dullness, agitation, decreased health and emotional damage.

These days I am adopting more of an Ayurvedic approach to alcohol in that I consume it occasionally. I feel more vibrant and high-energy when I have a few glasses per month and lethargic when I consume it on a regular basis.

#3 Early vs. Late Dinner

The late dinner time of Italians is linked, historically, to the country's climate because, during the summer, it is too hot to have dinner early. Over time this became a habit. Typically, Italian work schedules differ from other countries. In Italy, there is a 2-hour break in the middle of the day known as an afternoon riposo (rest time). So oftentimes, individuals finish work around 5 or 6 pm, they go back home or out for an aperitivo, then have a later dinner.

According to Ayurveda, it is preferable to have dinner between 5-7pm for optimal digestion. The last part of the day is dominated by kapha, therefore, whatever we eat must be able to balance kapha and not increase it.

These days I adopt an early dinner and enjoy having a meal between 6-7pm. I sleep better and I wake up with more energy. But as human beings we are adaptable. When I go back and visit my Italian family & community, I end up eating a late dinner and it doesn't really affect me so much.

#4 Espresso

Espresso is not only the most consumed beverage in Italy, it is an essential daily ritual linked to the culture, traditions, and habits of Italians. It is a veritable institution that has become part of the national identity for which Italians are recognized and appreciated throughout the world. Il Caffè is an unavoidable part of the Italians' life: they consume it, produce it, trade it, celebrate it and of course, talk about it. From the aroma, body, and crema, to blends, roasting, and grinding, basically, everything is discussed that revolves around the cup.

Although Ayurveda would never recommend that you supersize your daily cup of coffee, under the right conditions, at the right time, you can drink it in moderation. Know your dosha. Different mind-body types react to coffee differently, so it's important to determine your Ayurvedic constitution and make choices accordingly.

This was a tough habit for me to adjust to when I first moved to the United States. Eight years later, I find myself drinking one cup of coffee per day with occasional breaks from it when necessary. When I go back to Italy, I tend to adopt the cultural habit of having 2-3 espressos per day.

#5 Meal Courses

Menus in Italy are broken down by course to replicate the flow of a traditional Italian meal. Typically, each course is served in the order it appears on the menu from antipasto moving on through primi, secondi, contorni, and finally dolci. Many restaurants offer additional courses including aperitivo, insalata (salad), formaggio (cheese), frutta (fruit), caffè, "grappa" or "digestivo" (an after dinner alcoholic drink made from the skins of wine grapes), and although not officially a course, a favorite across Italy tagliere (charcuterie board)!

In Ayurveda, on the other hand, there is no such thing as sitting down and having meal courses. There is no rhythm to a meal, rather you're eating many flavors at once.

I like the meal courses because I associate a feeling of family and community gathering around a table for hours. After years of studying ancient Ayurvedic Medicine, I came to the conclusion that a long Italian meal with courses is often too hard to digest and it overloads the digestive system. So I always like to practice myself and say to others "always listen to your body to know when you are full".

#6 Breakfast

Breakfast in Italy is a sweet and enjoyable awakening routine for body and mind.

The staples of this meal are usually coffee (more rarely tea) and brioches ("croissant") or pane, burro e marmellata (bread, usually with a thin spread of butter and jam on top).

Light, warm and nutritious, oatmeal forms the basis of an Ayurvedic breakfast. It provides sustainable energy without overloading your digestive system. Plus, this tasty meal is quick to prepare.

These days I only indulge in my favorite Italian sweet breakfast every once in a while. So typically, I like to take the Ayurveda route and start my day with a nutritious oatmeal bowl or something savory to kick start my day without spiking my blood sugar.

EATING
as a ritual

If you ever visit a small town in Italy, you will notice that for Italians, the rhythm of life revolves around mealtimes. Food goes beyond just fuel and nourishment. It is what they live for.

Italians always say "In Italy, it is all about the food." Well, this is very true! In fact, **food represents the biggest expression of our culture.** It is a way to enjoy and socialize around a nice meal, a festival, a family celebration, or an event.

One thing that I was reminded of during my most recent visit to Italy was that everyone, including businesses that are not restaurants, closed for the lunch break. Il Pranzo (lunch) is usually served from 12.30-2.30pm. Restaurants will reopen again for dinner, which is usually served from 7-11 pm. Everyone in Italy takes a break to sit at a table and honor a cooked meal. During this time of the day, the town quiets down, the birds become louder and if you pay enough attention, you can hear the sounds of people enjoying their meals: cutlery on plates, the glug of waiters pouring wine, and people laughing.

The typical eating rhythm of the day in Italy goes like this:

- A light breakfast, or la colazione, in the morning is usually a cup (6-8 oz) of cappuccino with a biscotti, croissant, cereal, or yogurt.

- Lunch, or il pranzo, is usually the biggest meal of the day. It's eaten between 12- 2:30pm with a plate of pasta or rice and a side of veggies, ending with an espresso. Quick lunches for Italians are panini (sandwiches), a slice of pizza, or piadina, which is like a tortilla only fluffier, with a choice of cheese, prosciutto (ham), and maybe veggies.

- Aperitivo before dinner is also an important part of Italian food culture. This is usually between 5-6:30pm. It is "happy hour" and typically includes snacks and one drink. This is an idyllic way to catch up with friends or spend time with colleagues after work, before it gets too late in the evening.

- Dinner, or la cena, is usually a lighter meal between 7-10pm. It is another opportunity to socialize with family and friends. It usually includes protein and veggies or a salad. After dinner, it is normal to have coffee, as well as digestivi, which are warming alcoholic drinks that are served after a big meal to aid digestion and capitalize on enjoyment.

IL RIPOSO

One thing I learned from my Italian culture is how restorative and vital the act of just resting can be, both mentally and physically. Without rest, life is not enjoyable. The Italian culture has embodied this concept for centuries. On the other side of the Atlantic Ocean, American society is different. A completely new world to my eyes. People are chasing money, power, success, and a wilder, faster pace of life. Like any addiction, people are out of control in their behaviors, feelings, and thinking, yet they believe they are normal.

This is progress in America. You always move forward, and there are no limits to how far you can go or how fast you can get there. Don't pause, don't reflect. You win or lose. Fast at any cost is the mantra.

I am guilty of adopting this new way of living during my first years in America. I felt like I had to fit in. I felt that if I were resting, I wasn't doing enough, so I kept going. Racing non-stop and living the perfect American Style, I remember getting frustrated while waiting over 20 minutes to get my food to go. Energetically, the fast pace was draining me! During my visit to Italy in the summer of 2022, I returned to my family home with this attitude. My family didn't waste time straightening me up. Italians are very fiery, passionate, and straightforward in their way of conveying what they think.

During a hot summer day in June, my oldest brother and I went on an adventure to look for a venue to take pictures for this book. While driving in his tiny manual gray Italian car, he turned to me and said, "You've got to chill out, sis. You are becoming too American." I immediately knew what he meant. In his sassy Italian voice, he went on, "Here in Italy, we have a different pace of life. In fact, in about 20 minutes, all the shops will close down for the afternoon siesta. Don't you remember?".

I didn't remember...until that moment. I felt a little ashamed that I had forgotten my Italian habits. And worse, I had replaced them. I looked down and then out the window on that summer day and felt grateful I was starting to remember my authentic self.

The following day, I adopted "L'ora del riposo" (the hour of rest). It's well known to all locals, including kids, that between 12-3pm, people are sleeping, resting, and/or reading. What I love most about this is that everyone, from the pharmacy to the barber shop, is on the same page. Once I started incorporating the siesta, my body began to relax after just a few days. My mind stopped racing. My soul started to rest. I finally started recharging my batteries and healing at a cellular level. What I was reminded most about "il riposo" in Italy is its stubbornness–its refusal to sacrifice time for money and its dedication to the art of pause. Italians are the teachers of "il dolce far niente", the sweetness of doing nothing.

Despite many controversial opinions about time and productivity, rest is essential in losing weight naturally and healing at a cellular level. So if you find yourself constantly working, hustling, and over-exercising, I would encourage you to find time to slow down, rest, and be in the present moment. I have clients who, before we start working together, eat healthy, organic food and exercise regularly, but they are not taking the time to decompress from stress, so they are not losing weight and are constantly feeling stuck.

Habits you can start integrating today to increase rest and connection with yourself as well as "mindfulness" in your daily life are:

MEDITATION

Mediation can give you a sense of calm, peace, and balance that can benefit both your emotional well-being and your overall health. You can also use it to relax and cope with stress by refocusing your attention on something calming. There are different modalities to practice meditation like sitting in silence and focusing on your breath, listening to a guided meditation, practicing visualization, transcendental meditation, chakra meditation, etc. Choose the one that feels right for you.

I recommend starting with a guided visualization meditation for 10 minutes in the morning. Why in the morning? It is best to set the tone of the day right. How do you think the rest of your day will be if you wake up late, brush your teeth, dress in a hurry, drink your coffee on the go, and walk straight into a meeting? I can tell you...it will be stressful! What if instead, you: wake up 30 minutes earlier, do 10 minutes of meditation, write in a gratitude journal for 5 minutes, and have breakfast before walking out the door? How do you think your day is going to be then?

When my clients start their days with meditation practice, they feel much more grounded, present, and less stressed. You only need to wake up 15-30 minutes earlier and because all you need is time and space, it's something that you can start practicing today.

WHITE SPACE

White Space is dedicated time, preferably scheduled into your calendar in advance, intended to allow (and sometimes force) you to zoom out, reflect, come up for air, relax, and refuel. Most of my clients say that before starting to work with me, they lived a life totally on the go without even realizing it. During our journey together, I ask them to introduce white space into their calendars to help switch off their "fight or flight response." They tell me that they have immediately noticed improvements in their lifestyle and quality of life.

NATURE TIME, FOREST BATHING, OR GROUNDING

Research indicates that time spent in nature **is connected to cognitive and mental health benefits and improvements in mood and emotional well-being.** The term "Forest Bathing" refers to a physiological and psychological practice that emerged in Japan in the 1980s. The exercise, also known as "Shinrin-yoku," was developed to achieve two goals: to be an antidote for tech burnout and to inspire residents to connect with and protect the country's green spaces.

Forest Bathing is open-ended in practice because there is no suggestion as to what an individual should experience. While guided experiences exist, forest bathing can be as simple as standing in nature and engaging with the smells, sounds, and sights the area provides you.

Forest bathing is similar to grounding (or earthing), which is direct skin contact with the vast supply of electrons on the earth's surface. This can be done with bare feet, hands, or various grounding systems. Emerging research reveals that direct physical contact of the human body with the earth's natural electric charge has positive effects on human physiology and overall health. Some benefits linked to earthing include: defusing the causes of inflammation, pain, and stress, as well as improving blood flow, energy, and sleep. These can generate a greater sense of well-being. These two methods are both key in connecting with yourself and maintaining balance throughout the day. I would suggest a minimum of 30 minutes-1 hour per day in nature for increased mind, body, and soul well-being.

THE DO'S
and donts in Italy

Italians spend most of their time eating or talking about food and drinks. So being invited to eat with the family or at a friend's house is an expression of love, affection, and warmth.

Here are some simple rules you could try if you'd like. Remember small lifestyle and dietary adjustments lead to big changes.

ITALIAN DO'S

- Cook with simple and fresh ingredients.

- Gather around a big family lunch every Sunday.

- Have fresh pane (bread) available with lunch and dinner to mop up the sauces and flavors left on their plates. This even has a name, fare la scarpetta, which literally translates to 'make the little shoe,' but really refers to wiping one's plate clean with a piece of bread.

- Have wine on the table at dinner or Sunday lunch. They drink red wine, vino rosso, with meat and white wine, vino bianco, with fish. Italians say salute instead of cheers, which literally translates to 'health.'

- Have their foods in courses, not all together. They start with antipasto, then have their first course, second course, salad, fruit, and il dolce (dessert).

- Have espresso to close a meal.

- Offer you coffee (or sometimes tea) whenever you visit their home.

- Only use extra virgin olive oil, salt and/or vinegar for a salad dressing.

- Have three main meals a day, lunch being the biggest.

- Walk/bike everywhere.

ITALIAN DON'TS

- Never put chicken in pasta or on pizza.

- Never put pineapple on pizza.

- Usually, they do not have meat with pasta, although there are some exceptions.

- Do not put butter or pour extra virgin olive oil on their bread; as mentioned before, they simply use one piece to lap up the remnants of their meal.

- Usually do not have a savory breakfast.

- Rarely (If not ever) use barbecue sauce on meat.

- Do not have a big dinner.

- Don't have cappuccino after 11 am or with any other meal beside their breakfast.

- Do not continue to snack throughout the day.

A note about
FITNESS

The health benefits of regular exercise and physical activity are hard to ignore. Everyone benefits from exercise, regardless of age, sex, or physical ability.

Exercise is key to a balanced lifestyle. It supports detoxification through sweating while improving digestion, circulation, elimination, and lymphatic flow. Beyond that, movement brings rejuvenation to the body by helping release accumulated tensions, clearing stagnant emotions, and improving relaxation.

There are far too many people living a sedentary lifestyle these days, making movement and exercise more important than ever.

Is it possible to over-exercise?

We live in a society that reinforces the idea of exercising and being thin, making it very difficult to grasp the idea of balance. It is sad to say that exercise is used for people to reward themselves with a treat at the end of the day. This is a conditional way of loving themselves and reinforces the toxic diet cycle most people live in. Phrases like "No Pain, No Gain", "Push It", "Go Big or Go Home", "Just Do It", "Feel the Burn" are painful ways to shame people through exercise.

But remember that the key to longevity is balance. I see so many people living in extremes. They either live a sedentary lifestyle with minimal daily movement or they exercise too much. Neither of those options is healthy.

What is balance? Balance is a way of living in the absence of extremes.

In Ayurveda, balance is living mindfully according to your dosha, your mind-body constitution, and following the relative diet and lifestyle guidelines for it. A graceful approach to fitness is recognizing that each individual is unique and has different needs. Generally, it is best to exercise during kapha time of day, from about 6–10 a.m. and p.m. These times of day are ruled by kapha dosha and are therefore infused with a sense of groundedness, stability, and strength that helps counteract the inherent lightness and mobility of physical activity.

Beyond the generalities, it is important to tailor exercise to our unique dosha.

EXERCISE FOR YOUR BODY TYPE

VATA: Vatas benefit from grounding and calming exercises such as yoga, walking, cycling, and dancing. If anxiety is present, then relaxing, subtle exercises such as Tai Chi, Qi Gong, or Restorative Yoga are extremely healing.

PITTA: Pittas can enjoy long-distance cycling, running, or the above challenging sports. Exercising outside, especially in a beautiful, green area, is very healing to Pittas. Long walks in nature, hiking, or gardening are beneficial. Swimming is extremely ideal as the water cools the heat of a Pitta and helps to relieve stress and tension.

KAPHA: Kaphas excel at endurance sports and any sport that requires a lot of power, such as long-distance running/ walking, aerobics, dance, weight lifting, and rowing. Exercises that produce an aerobic effect and cause sweat are necessary to keep a Kapha in balance. This counterbalances their health issues of weight gain, congestion, and sluggishness.

A NOTE ABOUT MEDITATION

You have probably heard about meditation these days.

We all have mixed feelings about it, and I am going to express my opinion on what meditation really helps you to achieve. But before I do that, I would like to point out that when I was first introduced to meditation, I ended up ditching it after several months of consistently doing it. Why? Because I was getting frustrated. I thought it was hard, my head was spinning, and I felt like I was going nowhere.

During the months I was not practicing meditation, I started noticing that I was feeling ungrounded. What I realized is that sometimes you need to go back to the old ways to really understand how far you've grown.

Meditation is the art of stillness. It's about training in awareness and getting a healthy sense of perspective. You're not trying to turn off your thoughts or feelings. You're learning to observe them without judgment. There are different versions of meditation: mindfulness, spiritual, focused, movement, mantra, transcendental, visualization, etc.

Start with the type of meditation that suits you best at this time. Start consistently for 10 minutes and slowly increase the time when it feels right to do so.

What is

AYURVEDA

WHAT IS AYURVEDA?

Ayurveda is not a diet. It is a system that offers practical tools for both food and lifestyle. It teaches us that we cannot separate mind and body–for what affects the body affects our emotions, and our emotions affect our body. It is a holistic view of the individual that offers a unique treatment for each person. Surprisingly, Ayurveda and Italian Culture share some interesting similarities, even though they come from different geographical origins. I am excited to explain this connection to you.

Ayurveda, a natural system of medicine, originated in India more than 5,000 years ago. The term Ayurveda is derived from the Sanskrit words ayur (life) and veda (science or knowledge). Thus, Ayurveda translates to knowledge of life. Ayurveda places great emphasis on prevention and encourages the maintenance of health through close attention to balance in one's life–right thinking, diet, lifestyle, and the use of herbs. Knowledge of Ayurveda enables one to understand how to create this balance of body, mind, and consciousness according to one's own individual constitution and how to make lifestyle changes to bring about and maintain this balance.

The main principles of Ayurveda are:

- **Treat the root cause** of the illness—rather than respond to indicators of disease (aka treating the symptoms) - **by maintaining balance in and** harmony between your body, mind, soul, and environment.

- **Mind-Body Connection.** According to Ayurveda, the mind and body are connected, so what affects the physical body (diet, lifestyle, substance abuse) affects the mind. Vice versa, the mind has a very powerful influence on our overall health and well-being. Even very minor disturbances in our mental well-being can have the potential to negatively affect, not just the quality of our life situation, but also our physical health. In more extreme cases, it can lead to a whole range of diseases. Unresolved anger, for example, can accumulate in the liver and impair its functioning, unprocessed grief can impair the functioning of the lungs, and chronic anxiety can disturb colon health.

- Ayurveda heals through opposites. It is a science that is based on the laws of nature. One of the ways that Ayurveda utilizes the laws of nature is with a simple premise: **LIKE INCREASES LIKE. OPPOSITE QUALITIES BRING BALANCE.** So what does this mean? **Take in opposite qualities through the five senses.** This brings balance. For example: treat hot with cold. You already know this. When you are hot, you take your sweater off. Same with food. When you are hot or experience any inflammation, acid reflux, heartburn, or diarrhea, avoid eating/drinking hot, spicy, sugary foods like cayenne pepper, chili, alcohol, or fried foods that increase the same fire energy in the body. Choose cooling herbs like mint, fennel, cumin, and coriander; drink cooling drinks like fresh lemonade, peppermint tea, rose water, and coconut water; and avoid spicy meals.

The basics to remember are:

- **Treat cold with warmth**

- **Treat hot with cold**

- **Treat dryness with moistness**

- **Treat heaviness with lightness**

- **Treat mobility with stability**

Get the picture? Think of your own life and what qualities predominate. Then consider how to bring balance by bringing in the opposite qualities. Ayurveda is very empowering; it is a system of medicine that, once understood, places the tools for your own healing in your own hands!

DOSHAS

According to Ayurveda, every living entity has energy and life force, also referred to as prana (or chi in Chinese medicine). Ayurvedic medicine is based on the idea that the world is made up of five elements — aakash (space), jala (water), prithvi (earth), teja (fire), and vayu (air).

A combination of each element results in three humors, or doshas, known as Vata, Pitta, and Kapha. These doshas are believed to be responsible for a person's physiological, mental, and emotional health.

A person's unique ratio between humors (or bio-energy centers) is believed to make up the individual's mind-body constitution, a blueprint to achieve optimal health.

Let's take a look at what each dosha looks like.

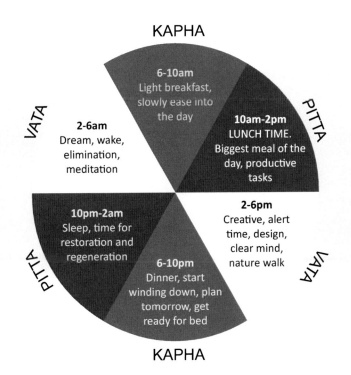

Ayurveda doesn't only reference the elements of nature, but also helps people understand how to best utilize their energy during different times of the day.

VATA

Elements – Air and Ether

Qualities

- Dry
- Light
- Cold
- Subtle
- Rough
- Mobile
- Clear

Season: Later Fall, Early Winter

Time of Life: 60+, Menopause and Beyond

Time of Day: 2-6 AM/PM

Tastes that Balance Vata: Sweet, Sour, Salty

Tastes that Increase Vata: Bitter, Pungent, Astringent

Vata consists of mainly two elements, air and ether, so it is usually considered the lightest dosha. It is represented by wind energy.

Vata governs any kind of movement in the mental and physical body, such as the circulatory system, transportation of nutrients and thoughts and signals from and to different organs.

Individuals with this predominant energy are usually physically light and slim with flexible bodies, small irregular teeth, and small, dry, active eyes.

They are usually very creative and are easily excited. They are known for thinking outside the box, but their energy comes in bursts. Because of this, they are likely to experience sudden fatigue.

As they have a sensitive digestive system, they are naturally more prone to digestive and malabsorption problems, due to having an irregular appetite and thirst. They are delicate in health, and their sleep is light and disturbed.

Emotionally, they are quick to act without thinking and are known to have an "emotional lover, buyer" personality. They love new experiences and they are always looking for new adventures. In fact, they do not like sitting on the couch for a long time!

Strengths: learn quickly, highly creative, multitasker, kind-hearted, flexible, "on the go," naturally slim, prone to change.

Weaknesses: forgetful, anxious, unstable mood, can get overwhelmed easily, highly sensitive to the cold, trouble sleeping, irregular appetite and eating patterns, prone to digestive issues and gas, poor circulation (cold hands and feet).

PITTA

Elements – Water and Fire

Qualities

- Hot
- Sharp
- Light
- Liquid
- Spreading
- Oily
- Fleshy

Season: Late Spring, Summer

Time of Life: Puberty - Menopause

Time of Day: 10-2 AM/PM

Tastes that Balance Pitta: Sweet, Bitter, Astringent

Tastes that Increase Pitta: Salty, Sour, Pungent

Pitta consists mainly of two elements, fire and water. It is usually associated with a tenacious personality and is represented by fire energy.

Pitta governs any kind of transformation in the mental and physical body, such as any metabolic function and processing of thoughts and emotions.

Individuals with this predominant energy are usually physically medium, with a strong frame. They have intense (blue) eyes, but a sensitive gaze, sensitive skin with potential freckles, blonde or red hair, but balding or thinning and prematurely gray hair.

They usually have a fair complexion, strong appetite, lots of energy and like cooling drinks.

As they have strong digestion, sometimes it can cause hyperacidity, acid reflux, or a burning sensation in the body. In fact, Pitta people have warm body temperatures. They sleep soundly for short periods of time.

Emotionally, Pitta people have a fiery nature that manifests in both body and mind. They have excellent learning, understanding, and concentration skills. They are natural leaders (goal driven/competitive) and well-disciplined.

When balanced, Pitta shows understanding and intelligence. Out of balance, Pitta tends to become angry, judgmental, critical, and jealous, all of which can generate inflammation disorders.

Strengths: intelligent, purposeful, learns quickly, self-determined, masters skills easily, a strong desire for success, strong, natural leader, quick metabolism, good circulation, healthy skin and hair.

Weaknesses: impatient, prone to conflict, always hungry, mood swings when hungry, prone to acne and inflammation, sensitive to hot temperatures.

KAPHA

Elements – Water and Earth

Qualities

- Heavy
- Slow
- Cool (cold)
- Smooth (soft)
- Dense
- Oily
- Static

Season: Late Winter, Early Spring

Time of Life: Birth until Puberty

Time of Day: 6-10 AM/PM

Tastes that Balance Kapha: Pungent, Bitter, Astringent

Tastes that Increase Kapha: Sweet, Sour, Salty

Kapha consists mainly of two elements, earth and water. It is usually associated with a grounded and compassionate personality and is represented by earth energy.

Kapha governs any kind of structure in the mental and physical body, such as hydrating all cells and frameworks, lubricating the joints, saturating the skin, maintaining immunity, safeguarding the tissues, and regulating our ability to feel contentment.

Individuals with this predominant energy are usually physically strong, thick-boned, and caring. They have large and soft eyes, strong teeth, thick, curly hair, and oily smooth skin.

Kapha people tend to have a steady appetite and thirst but tend to have slow digestion and metabolism. When Kapha builds to an excess, it often results in weight gain and mucus production, causing allergies to manifest in the body. At times, cravings for sweet and salty lead to water retention.

Emotionally, when they are balanced, Kaphas are naturally calm and loving. They have stable faith and compassion and a steady mind. They have a good memory, a deep voice, and a monotonous pattern of speech. They love eating, sitting, doing nothing, and sleeping for a long time.

When out of balance, they suffer from greed, attachment, possessiveness, and laziness.

Strengths: empathetic, caring, trusting, patient, calm, wise, happy, romantic, strong bones and joints, healthy immune system.

Weaknesses: prone to weight gain, slow metabolism, sluggishness, oversleeping, breathing issues (i.e., asthma, allergies), higher risk of heart disease, mucus buildup, susceptible to depression, need regular motivation and encouragement.

CHAKRA SYSTEM

In Sanskrit, the word "chakra" means "disk" or "wheel" and refers to the energy centers in your body. These wheels or disks of spinning energy each correspond to specific nerve bundles and major organs. They can be either excessive or deficient. To function at their best, your chakras need to stay open or balanced. You may experience physical or emotional symptoms related to a particular chakra if it gets blocked.

Seven main chakras run along your spine. They start at the root, or base, of your spine and extend to the crown of your head.

Root Chakra (Muladhara)

The first Chakra, or Muladhara, is located at the base of the spine. It is usually represented by the color red. It provides the foundations of life and helps you feel grounded and able to withstand challenges. The root chakra is where we feel safe or in danger, therefore it's responsible for your sense of security and stability.

The mantra for the root Chakra is "I am safe."

When out of balance, a person may experience ungroundedness, fear, financial constraints, feeling unsafe or unsupported, anxiety, weak joints, and stiff muscles.

If you feel depleted and unstable in your first Chakra, try these tips.

- Meditate for 15-20 minutes per day. Meditation helps to clear the mind and come back to the present moment.

- Ground yourself in nature. When you are grounded, you feel like you are here, present in this world. To be grounded gives your energy a

point of steadiness so you feel clear, centered, strong, and focused.

- Consume more cooked root vegetables and protein-rich foods to help you ground your energy.

- Use stones and crystals like red jasper, smoky quartz, hematite, cuprite, mahogany obsidian, tourmaline, rhodonite, garnet, and bloodstone.

- Practice yoga poses like wild child pose, seated forward bend pose, garland pose, chair pose, and dangling pose.

Sacral Chakra (Svadisthana)

The second Chakra, or Svadisthana, is located just below your belly button. It is usually represented by the color orange. This Chakra is responsible for your sexual and creative energy.

The mantra for the sacral Chakra is "I am creative."

When out of balance, a person may experience low creativity, feeling stuck, low libido, lower back pain, and fertility issues.

If you feel depleted and unstable in your second Chakra, try these tips.

- Practice yoga postures that target the sacral area. Some of these poses include happy baby, goddess, butterfly, cobra, and seated torso circles.

- Use stones and crystals to balance the sacral Chakra, like unakite, carnelian, snowflake obsidian, orange calcite, red jasper, and sunstone.

- Tap into your creative side. Even if you feel

you're lacking in artistic inspiration right now, tapping into your creative side can help revive this energy center.

- Tap into your sensual side. Are you scared of pleasure or feeling a lack of desire? Sometimes acknowledging the blockage is the first step in helping the energy flow.

- Consume more sweet, warm foods that are nourishing and orange in color: carrots, peaches, apricots, sweet potatoes, and mangos.

Solar Plexus (Manipura)

The third Chakra, or Manipura, is located in your stomach area. It is usually represented by the color yellow. It's responsible for confidence and self-esteem and helps you feel in control of your life.

The mantra for the sacral Chakra is "I am strong. I am worthy."

When out of balance, the person may experience low self-esteem, lack of willpower, lack of worthiness, digestive issues, and back problems.

If you feel depleted and unstable in your third Chakra, try these tips.

- Practice asana postures that target the solar plexus area. Some of these postures are boat pose, bow pose, and warrior pose.

- Use stones and crystals to balance the third Chakra, like citrine, amber, calcite, tigers eye, pyrite, yellow jasper, yellow topaz, agate, yellow tourmaline, and lemon quartz.

- Spend a minimum of 20 minutes in sunlight each day.

- Consume yellow foods like bananas, pineapple, corn, lemons, and yellow curry.

- Tap into your sense of self-worth. What limiting beliefs are you holding onto about yourself or your experience?

Heart Chakra (Anahata)

The fourth Chakra, or Anahata, is located at the center of your chest and represents the heart center. It is usually represented by the color green. The heart is an energetic center of the body. The lower three Chakras govern the connection with the outer world (family, relationship, finance, our work in the world), and the three upper Chakras are all about the inner life – a spiritual aspect of who we are. The Heart Chakra is the bridge between the outer world and inner world.

The mantra for the heart chakra is "I am loved."

When out of balance, a person may experience chest tightness, breathing problems (asthma), grief, codependency, poor boundaries, and intense jealousy or possessiveness. They may also be withdrawn, judgmental, depressed, and develop a fear of intimacy and getting hurt in relationships.

If you feel depleted and unstable in your fourth Chakra, try these tips.

- **Practice asana postures that target the chest area.** Some of these postures are high lunges with shoulder openers, wild thing & upward-facing dog.

- **Use stones and crystals** to balance the heart chakra, like rose quartz, amazonite, aventurine, and rhodochrosite.

- **Drink heart-opening beverages** like rose tea and cacao.

- **Practice gratitude.** Keep a gratitude journal, writing down three things a day that you feel grateful for.

- **Consume green foods** like spinach, kale, broccoli, cauliflower, cabbage, and green tea.

Throat Chakra (Vishuddha)

The fifth Chakra, or Vishuddha, is located at the base of the throat and is related to self-expression. It is usually represented by the color blue.

The throat chakra represents the element 'Ether or Space,' therefore it is associated with Vata Dosha.

The mantra of the throat chakra is *"I am expressive".*

When the throat Chakra is blocked, the person may have a fear of speaking, difficulty putting feelings into words, become introverted, or develop strep throat, thyroid issues, and jaw tightness.

If you feel depleted and unstable in your fifth Chakra, try these tips.

- **Practice yoga poses** like shoulder stand, plow, and fish — which release the neck muscles.

- **Use stones and crystals** to balance the throat chakra, such as lapis lazuli, turquoise, aquamarine, and celestite.

- **Consume blue foods** like blueberries, blackberries, coconut water, juicy plums, lemons, apples, and pears.

- **Practice speaking your truth** even if it feels uncomfortable at times.

Third Eye Chakra (Ajna)

The sixth Chakra, or Ajna, is located at the center of our forehead. It is usually related to the center of our inner vision and intuition. It is usually represented by the color indigo.

The third eye chakra represents the element 'Light,' and it is centered around our awareness, wisdom, imagination, perception, clairvoyant abilities, and spiritual communication. It is related to our ability to see – both physically and intuitively, and it's about elevating our consciousness and challenging ourselves to see from a different perspective. When this Chakra is blocked, a person may experience a lack of trust in their intuitive "readings" of people or situations.

The mantra of the third eye chakra is *"I am connected."*

If you feel depleted and unstable in your sixth Chakra, try these tips.

- **Use stones and crystals** to balance the third eye chakra, such as amethyst, purple sapphire, and purple violet tourmaline.
- **Consume purple foods** like purple carrots, grapes, eggplants, purple cabbage, and blueberries.
- **Meditate** to activate the pineal gland through vibration and intention.
- **Ground yourself in nature** to center your energy and regain a connection with yourself.

Crown Chakra (Sahasrara)

The seventh Chakra, or Sahasrara, is located at the top of your head and governs the pituitary glands. It is represented by the colors violet and white. It is associated with the central nervous system and represents the spirit of our mind and body.

The mantra of the crown chakra is *"I am divine."*

Through the seventh Chakra, **we cultivate the right knowledge,** and wisdom, transcending consciousness and understanding, and are connected to the divine source.

When this Chakra is blocked, a person may experience confusion, a lack of connection to the world, a lack of focus, and overall poor coordination.

If you feel depleted and unstable in your seventh Chakra, try these tips.

- **Use stones and crystals** to balance the crown chakra, such as amethyst, clear quartz, selenite, lepidolite, howlite, labradorite, and moonstone.
- **Meditate** with the intention to connect with the Divine Source.
- **Ground yourself in nature** to center your energy and regain a connection with the spirit world.
- **Practice journaling** after meditation and writing down any downloads that come through because these will be essential messages from the Divine Source.

MAINTAINING HEALTH
with Ayurveda

According to Ayurveda, diet has one of the most direct impacts on the three Doshas/humors. To keep these Doshas balanced, our diet should contain all Tastes (Rasas) in a balanced way. For a healthy person, Ayurveda advises not to fill your stomach completely from eating. The stomach should be divided into three portions: one portion should be filled by food, the second with water, and the third should be kept vacant for the movement of Doshas (Humors). The right quantity of food is decided by the nature of food substances, such as the heaviness or lightness of what you're eating as well as your specific digestive power.

Diet plays a very important role in the status of both our physical and mental health. Many common health problems can be prevented or treated by eating a healthy diet. The following guidelines should be followed:

- Wash vegetables & fruits properly before cooking.

- Use boiling, steaming, grilling, etc. as methods of cooking.

- It is desirable to eat 50-100 grams a day of fiber.

- Increase the amount of locally available seasonal fruits and green leafy vegetables that you eat on a daily basis.

- As much as possible, eat freshly prepared food. Refrigerating and reheating food tends to decrease both taste and nourishment.

- Eat when you feel hungry i.e. don't avoid mealtimes. Develop the habit of taking meals at regular intervals.

- Avoid overeating.

- Avoid eating too fast or too slow. Food eaten hurriedly does not get digested properly. It doesn't give you a sense of fulfillment, so you tend to eat more.

- Don't drink too much water or too little water since both hamper digestion. Ayurveda emphasizes on **drinking water only when you feel thirsty.** Every person has a different body, hence, drinking the same amount of water cannot be recommended to everybody.

- Drinking lukewarm water helps urine and bowel movement flow, enhances digestive power, minimizes diseases related to the digestive system, and delays aging.

- Don't eat when your mind is unstable because you may eat too little or too much.

- Avoid heavy tasks immediately after meals since blood circulation will be diverted towards the site of action rather than towards the digestion of food. This also creates pressure on the heart.

- Dinner should be eaten at least two hours before you go to sleep.

- Reduce your intake of fried foods, salt, and sugar making them an occasional treat rather than a daily habit.

- Avoid drinking carbonated drinks (soda) and eating fast foods.

- Increase your intake of fermented dairy, i.e., Kefir, Lassi and nourishing drinks, such as coconut water, probiotics, etc.

- Food should be eaten calmly, without any disturbances.

- After meals, rinse your mouth and hands thoroughly with water.

Daily Routine (Dinacharya)

The tradition of dinacharya (daily routine) is one of the single most powerful Ayurvedic tools for improving overall health and well-being. It refers to a daily self-care routine. It can be summarized as follows:

- **Wake up** early, at least before 6 am.

- **Attending nature's call** (Malotsarg): bowels, urination etc. Never suppress nor forcefully void the natural urges - Vegavidharan (suppression) can lead to many diseases. After defecation, the anal area should be cleaned properly with water and hands should be washed properly with soap.

- **Care of Teeth.** Using fresh sticks of Neem (Azadirachta indica), Khadir (Acacia catechu) etc. can clean teeth and dissipate any foul smell.

- **Nasal drops** (Nasya). Put two drops, one in each nostril, of sesame oil/ mustard oil/ ghee. It soothes and protects the nasal passage while nourishing the tissues. Daily nasal lubrication helps to release tension in the head and relieve accumulated stress.

- **Mouth wash** (Gandush). Fill your mouth with a Triphala decoction or other medicated oils. This prevents excess thirst, improves taste, and maintains oral hygiene. It is also useful in managing mouth ulcers and dryness commonly seen in Diabetes patients.

- **Self-massage** (Abhyanga). The application of oil daily. Keeps skin soft, improves blood circulation, and removes waste. Apply Tila (Sesame) oil or any suitable oil on your head in a sufficient quantity, which enhances the strength of the head and forehead and makes hair long, and deep-rooted.

- **Exercising** early in the morning can help remove stagnation in your body and can help recharge and rejuvenate your body and mind for a productive day. Regular exercise is an important step in the prevention and management of various ailments.

- **Food** (Bhojan). A balanced diet for your dosha should be followed.

- **Sleep** (Nidra). Keep your environment clean and pleasant. Avoid sleeping during the day. Proper sleep provides health and longevity and improves complexion and glow. One should sleep between 6-8 hours per night. In the summer, you can also take a small nap during the day. Too much sleep and too little sleep are not good for healthy living.

The Shushruta Samhita (an ancient Sanskrit text) allows for short afternoon naps in the summer because **summer is the one season that most effectively balances Kapha and Vata**. *The summer's heat helps to dry up excess Kapha and also warms Vata, the first dosha to become imbalanced with sleep deprivation or overexertion.*

Spiritual Weight Loss

TREATING THE ROOT CAUSE,
not the symptoms

If you believe in the connection between the mind and the body, and you're familiar with what a "holistic approach" means, then this chapter will make sense to you. If you are new to this concept, I hope this chapter will help you understand and broaden your horizons. If I had a dollar for every client who said "I am eating healthy and exercising, but my weight is not moving," I'd have enough money to buy a house.

If you're eating healthy and exercising, why are you still struggling to lose and/or maintain weight? Or worse, sliding backward? Here is the truth: it is not that you are a failure or that you don't have the willpower. It's that there is something you are not considering.

You have been conditioned to think that in order to lose weight, you need only to focus on a healthy diet and exercise. But that's not the whole story. You're not a computer. You can't just plug in some numbers and magically change your life. You are a human and you need to be treated as a whole being instead of isolating one area

of your life from another. It is all interconnected. Your nutrition affects your mental health and your emotions affect your body. This is the foundation of the **mind-body connection.**

This is the part that so many people don't understand and don't implement. It's like preparing cake batter and forgetting to bake it. You miss the point of the whole exercise. Why did you mix all of those ingredients together in the first place? If you continue to live in the ignorance that there is no mind-body connection, you will miss out on the best part of this journey.

For so many of you, uncovering the reasons that are affecting your health (the root causes) is the hardest part of the process. People have a hard time looking inside at what they have created, but in order to move forward, we must take responsibility for what we have allowed to happen to our health. It's so easy to want a quick fix: "Just give me a diet that makes me lose weight and that's it." But your body doesn't work like that. And if you keep doing the same things, your body will resist your power struggle and gain all of the weight back (if not more). It is not a rewarding, happy path. Trust me. I walked that path for a while, until I realized that I was walking the wrong way.

Don't worry. I will guide you through the process so it feels easier to understand. The steps I am about to explain might just be the breakthrough you need to finally meet your goals. If you are truly desiring to break through and heal once and for all, these steps are the key to success.

It is time to dig beneath the surface and uncover what else is affecting you. These areas are the non-physical, not-so-evident aspects of your life that affect your health and trigger healthy/unhealthy behaviors. They affect your life as much as your nutrition does.

There are four main areas that affect health (in no particular order):

1. RELATIONSHIPS

2. JOB/PURPOSE

3. POSITIVE SELF-TALK

4. SOUL INJURY (trauma stored in the body)

When these things are balanced, there is harmony. But when your awareness has been buried under a pile of dirt, we suffer. According to Ayurveda, the **body** is a **crystallization of our mind.** So just as an impaired digestive system and poor gut health create diseases, unprocessed emotions can also lead to disease in very physical ways. For example, unresolved anger can accumulate in the liver and impair its functioning, unprocessed grief can disturb the lungs, and chronic anxiety can upset the health of the colon. There are countless other ways that imbalances in the mind can manifest as physical disease.

Emotions start with **thoughts.** Thoughts create a chemical reaction in our brains, which lead to emotions. And emotions can affect any system or cell in the body. For instance, you're thinking about going on vacation in one week. Thinking about taking a break and not working sparks a chemical reaction that you perceive as joy and excitement. This flow of positive emotions translates into feeling excited about going on walks/hikes during your vacation, journaling, reading that book you haven't yet started, or eating healthier, drinking more water, etc.

On the other hand, the thought of getting back to a job you deeply dislike feels like death. The thought of coming back to a reality you hate sparks a reaction in your body–you feel trapped and disappointed, and every day feels worse. These emotions might affect your daily life in significant ways. You don't feel excited to eat healthily because you are stressed out or you don't see the point in working out and/or changing your habits because you are so entangled in a spiral of negative emotions.

If an area (that is not food or exercise) is creating stress in your life, know that your body doesn't know how to distinguish between the stress of running from a tiger and the stress of working at a job you hate.

RELATIONSHIPS

This isn't just about your romantic relationship, it's also the relationships you have with family members, friends, and other individuals that are part of your daily life.

I'd like to invite you to think of the five closest relationships that you have and ask yourself these questions: Are they supportive of me and where I am going? Are they open-minded? Are they ready to stand beside me as I'm trying to figure myself out? As I improve my lifestyle, will they support the changes I am trying to make?

According to Jim Rohn, motivational speaker, and self-help guru, "You are the average of the five people you spend the most time with." What he is saying is that **who you spend time with influences the person you eventually become. Who you are with can elevate you as much as it can bring you down.**

To be clear, I am not inviting you to make any drastic changes and purge people out of your life. I'm inviting you to think of the people that have an influence in your life and ask yourself if they elevate you or bring you down. After acknowledging the truth of your relationships (that deep down you already know), I'd like to invite you to think outside of the box. Can you find a new like-minded community—in person and/or online—who can uplift your energy with daily/weekly conversations and help you feel connected?

Acknowledging and expressing this truth and taking steps in the right direction may be just what you need to unlock your energy and improve your health.

JOB/ PURPOSE

"Living your purpose" means doing what truly matters to you in alignment with your values and beliefs. I can't tell you what that means for you, but you know it when you feel it—and when you don't.

You can be living your purpose at your 9-5 job, as a stay-at-home parent, or as the CEO of a company. The important thing is the feeling of general contentment. Being stuck in this area affects your happiness, your health, and your relationships. It can be very painful. However, when you are true to yourself and living your purpose, life takes on a whole new meaning. You feel fulfilled, happy, and free.

Take Joanie, for example, she was working a 9-5 job that she actually enjoyed at first. After 10+ years in a toxic environment where her talents and hard work were not being appreciated she started to feel very tired and sad. Suddenly she started experiencing daily fatigue. She called her doctors and had a blood test done. The results came back just fine. During one of our life coaching sessions, she came to realize she needed to give her two weeks' notice. It was time to move on. Once she did, she started noticing her energy coming back in a matter of days. Her fatigue was lifting like a dark cloud after a storm.

POSITIVE SELF-TALK

One of the most important relationships you have is the one you have with yourself. Because of this, it is crucial that you recognize your self-talk. Is it lifting you up or bringing you down?

Your **inner dialogue** is very important to achieving the success of your goals. It can be positive or negative, and it sets the foundation for your mindset. Mindset is the collection of beliefs and thoughts that make up the mental attitude, inclination, habit, or disposition that predetermines a person's interpretations and responses to events, circumstances, and situations. It is everything.

It's pretty hard to make positive long-lasting changes when you are hard on yourself and pick on yourself every five minutes. For example, if you are creating the new healthy habit of meditating every morning for 10-20 min, but one day you don't do it. Life happens. What do you do? Most people start their negative rampage with "You fell off the wagon, you are already failing, why bother to continue if you can't follow through?" Do you see where this negative self-talk is leading? It's leading you to give up and reinforces the belief (you already have) that you are failing.

What if instead you say, "I couldn't do it this morning, but I am sure I can find 10 minutes sometime today to connect with myself. I love where I am going and the new healthy habits I am establishing. It is going to take time to do this consistently, but I am learning, and I am not trying to be perfect. I am a human trying to find balance". Do you see how this second self-talk is more encouraging, positive, and supportive? Change your self-talk and you will start seeing major improvements.

SOUL INJURY

Trauma body, also called soul *injury,* is a wound that separates a person from their sense of self—it impacts their entire being. The concept originated with a group of Veterans Administration (VA) hospice nurses who cared for 10,000 dying veterans; the nurses witnessed "soul injuries" firsthand as they resurfaced on combat veterans' deathbeds.

As an Intuitive Health & Life Coach, I often hear: "I'm eating somewhat healthy, I'm active, I've tried everything, but I'm not sure why I can't seem to get back to my normal weight or drop those last few pounds?" It feels like an enigma to many of us, but it isn't. Once you understand and accept that there is a mind-body-soul connection going on within you that can positively or negatively affect your overall wellness, it clicks. The work that I do goes beyond normal nutrition and lifestyle hacks to reach a healthy weight. Why? I look for the **root causes** of my client's **imbalanced state.**

When trauma occurs, in an effort to protect you, your brain temporarily pauses your memory processing system and the experience is stored differently than traditional memories are. Trauma is a **shock** to the **system.** When that shock is stored instead of released, it can cause physical and mental health issues down the road. Active memories of trauma remain locked and can cause blockages until a "trigger" occurs.

Emotional memories of traumatic life events are stored in the brain along with the anger, grief, worry, stress, and fear often associated with them. Research has now shown that emotional memories, both positive and negative, leave strong impressions on our brain, and therefore affect our behavior. There is a link between processes in the cell nucleus and the release of the enzyme calcineurin, which determines the intensity of emotional memories.

Emotion is energy in action and this energy from past trauma continues to live inside the survivor's body. The negative emotions attached to these past traumas block the healthy flow of energy within the body and can even create an environment for disease to exist, slowly developing over a lifetime.

A Kaiser study published in 1998 found that, as the number of ACEs (adverse childhood events) in a child's life increases, so does the likelihood of "multiple risk factors for several of the leading causes of death in adults," such as heart disease, cancer, chronic lung disease, and liver disease. Holding onto negative emotions in the cellular memory will ultimately cause physical and/or psychological distress.

Historically, the majority of us are taught to "move on" and "survive" our trauma. But is this really possible? The reality is that if the trauma remains unprocessed, it will get stored in the body and manifest itself as a potential physical or emotional symptom. Gut issues, weight gain, constipation, diarrhea, skin problems, depression, anxiety, Post Traumatic Stress Disorder (PTSD), as well as numerous other physical and mental issues, can all be a result of trauma.

Side effects of trauma can be severe, but there is good news: science shows us they can be reversed. Biochemical and brain imaging studies are demonstrating that the brain has a powerful ability, not only to survive trauma but to heal itself as well. While there are several methods to resolve trauma on cellular memory, let's explore a few that I use regularly.

A holistic approach means **providing support that looks at the whole person.** The support should consider a person's physical, emotional, social, and spiritual well-being. It does not isolate physical health from mental or spiritual health, because it is rooted in the belief that you are whole. You are mind, body, and soul. So what affects your body affects your mind and vice versa. Let me explain.

When you want to lose weight and you just focus on dieting, you are only focusing on one thing: the nutritional side of your body. But again, you are not just your body. What if the root cause of your weight gain was emotional? What if you are overeating because deep down you feel lonely or bored or sad? I would like to take you a bit further into an even deeper concept. What if your weight gain was coming from a spiritual injury? A spiritual injury is a traumatic experience that wounded your soul, and has been recorded in your subconscious mind. If you are now acting from that place, you may be gaining weight because deep down you are protecting yourself.

SUBCONSCIOUS MIND

*"Until you make the unconscious
conscious, it will direct your life and
you will call it fate."
~Carl Jung*

If you think you are making conscious decisions most of the time, think again. You're actually not.

Your subconscious mind is a powerful force. According to Harvard professor Gerald Zaltman, "95% of our purchase decision-making takes place in the subconscious mind." The 5% left is your conscious brain.

Your subconscious also holds all the "programs" that control the way you think, what you believe, the way you feel, act, react, and pretty much everything else that forms who you are. Its primary function is to follow the instructions of the conscious mind and it does this by proving whatever the conscious mind believes is true. In other words, the job of the subconscious mind is to prove the conscious mind is always right. If you consciously believe that you can't be, do or have something, then you are always right. The subconscious mind will get to work and create the circumstances and find the people to prove that you are right. So how do we take control of this?

First of all, did you know that all of your thoughts and beliefs aren't even yours? All those negative emotions and negative beliefs that swirl around in your head and interfere with your confidence, your self-worth, your ability to attract the right people and situations into your life, are literally not even yours.

What does this mean? These negative beliefs and emotions are "programs" in your subconscious mind which were formed between the ages of 0-7 years old. Yes, when you were just a little kid. It was during this time that your subconscious mind was formed.

Everything you saw, heard and felt was based on the environment and the adults around you. This molded your subconscious mind as you took on all of their beliefs! At this age, you did not have the critical faculty to reject anything that did not sit right with you, so, quite literally, your limiting thoughts and beliefs are not even yours.

Why am I introducing you to the subconscious mind?

Oftentimes women come to me because they want to lose weight and change their relationship with food. Maybe they have been dieting for years or have body dysmorphia or suffer from binging. It doesn't matter why they decide they have had enough. It does not depend on willpower. It comes down to their subconscious mind and the beliefs and trauma their body and mind are holding onto, preventing their health journey from improving.

Most of the time the reasons why you are not able to let go of the weight have nothing to do with food.

Janet, for example, came to me after healing her gut health with a good diet and supplement regimen but she was still craving sugar. She wanted to understand the root cause. During our session, we discovered that the root cause of the sugar craving was that she had never dealt with the loss of her ex-husband who passed prematurely. The root cause, in this case, was grief.

Aleesa, for example, had an intense craving for fast food that she could not overcome. She described it as "stronger than her will." When it came to leaving work and going home to her family, she felt out of control; sooner than she realized it, she inhaled a cheeseburger, fries, and a milkshake. After our healing session, she realized that every time she was triggered by loneliness subconsciously, she felt the need to compensate and comfort herself with fast foods.

To me the miracles I see every week are incredible. What I find the most fascinating is to watch my clients reprogram at a cellular memory and break destructive cycles when they face what is stored deep in their subconscious mind.

ENERGETIC CAUSES,
of weight gain

When people come to me struggling with body issues, they tend to focus on treating the symptoms of their body alone. What they don't realize is that by doing so, they will only get so far before their body reaches a plateau. The reality is that you can only get past a plateau by getting to the root causes of the *"beyond weight gain."*

Have you ever noticed the connection between a traumatic event or change in your life and sudden weight gain? Maybe you're even beginning to have digestive issues or other chronic health issues?

According to Dr. James Gordon (founder of the Center for Mind-Body Medicine), "The brain and peripheral nervous system, the endocrine and immune systems, and indeed, all the organs of our body and all the emotional responses we have, share a common chemical language and are constantly communicating with one another." This means that our thoughts, feelings, beliefs, and attitudes can positively (or negatively) affect our biological functioning. In other words, our minds literally affect how healthy our bodies are! For example, Louise L. Hay writes in her book, *You Can Heal Your Life*, that "Fat is related

to oversensitivity." She says that "anger at being denied love" can manifest as fat in our arms.

When I begin working with my clients, we start by balancing their physical body and addressing the unseen subtle causes of their weight gain. This helps us to know what is keeping them from losing the stubborn weight that just won't go away.

Part of what sets apart the weight loss strategy at Love Holistic Living is that we address the root cause of weight gain in the physical, emotional and spiritual body. This yields long-lasting results. All-natural. No diets, fads, or pills are required.

So, with this said, here are the *five* main energetic causes of weight gain that I find in my clients.

1. **Not feeling safe** in your body due to past trauma (i.e. physical, emotional, sexual abusive experiences/relationships). When I do energetic work on my clients, 90% of the time they are not in their body. Their very first chakra (one of the centers of spiritual power in the human body) isn't grounded or anchored. It should be very stable. So part of the work we do is helping them to regain a feeling of

safety. I bring them back into their physical body through energetic healing sessions.

2. **Fear of being seen or hiding.** This fear is oftentimes subconscious, so many people may not realize they have it. Losing weight and being attractive is scary for some women, especially so for women who have been hiding for a long time. Stepping into your power and beauty can feel intimidating. To be invisible may be a comfortable place for someone so that the world leaves you alone.

3. **Protection.** Are you afraid of getting hurt again? So much so that you have built a wall between you and the world? If so, fat cells could be protecting you by literally forming a cushion between you and the world. It's like using bubble wrap to protect your delicate china! This is a defense mechanism that can manifest when you are very sensitive, easily hurt, feel bullied, are verbally, physically or sexually abused, or generally feel unsafe.

4. **Survival Mode.** The fight or flight response is an automatic physiological reaction to an event that is perceived as stressful or frightening. The heart beats faster, blood pressure goes up, big muscles get tense and ready to run or fight, and digestion slows down. After a prolonged state of traumatic response, this can shock the autonomic nervous system into a state of hyperarousal and hypervigilance. When in survival mode, the tendency is to overeat to fill a void, consequently gaining weight.

5. **Lack of boundaries.** Oftentimes, lack of boundaries can be the cause of weight gain. When someone's responsibilities are greater than their ability to handle them, it can cause troubled sleep. Restlessness is one of the activators of the "stress response" in the nervous system, causing the body to stop digestion, increase cortisol levels, and accelerate heart rate and respiration in order to either fight or run away from the threat. It's important to have a healthy amount of stress, so try not to take on more than you can handle.

How do we shift and heal these subtle blockages?

Your body is the temple of your soul, no matter what it looks like. It is sacred. You have to accept yourself and whatever weight you are now. Then you can prime your body to look its best.

You can do this by using an affirmation such as... "I accept myself the way I am. I salute the divinity within me and I promise to maintain a healthy relationship between my body and my mind."

Or

"I love myself and I am committed to listening to my body's signals and making conscious choices around food."

Through my healing sessions, I oftentimes can pinpoint where the energy is stored. From there, I find out what the blockage is to move it through, and out of the person's body. Skeptics of this methodology have only to witness the tears, breakthroughs, and releases of severe pain, not to mention the life-giving after effects of this work to become not only believers but champions of it.

If you believe you might be holding onto negative emotions, here is a simple, 3 Step-Process to start the journey of releasing trauma in your body:

1. **Grounding. Send Roots into the Ground.** Notice your feet, or, if seated, your back, buttocks, and back of your legs in the chair. Now notice your feet or lower body being firmly connected to the floor, then to the ground, like roots growing deep into the earth. Take a deep breath. Then gaze about the room and notice objects or textures about the room, remaining connected to your "roots." For more information on the power of this technique, see my previous article "The Science of Grounding: Demystifying Earth's Healing Effects."

2. **Assessing. First,** notice your breath and breathe deep. Begin to scan your body from the top of your head, down to the heels of your feet. Notice any sensations that come up naturally and where that sensation shows up in your body. Is it in your shoulder, in your lower back, in your head, your gut..? There is no right or wrong answer, but, be present with what you are experiencing.

3. **Feeling and Discharging.** Bring to awareness a resource. A resource is anything that feels strong and calm to you. These can be a wise ancestor, a deity of your faith or even a pet. Using a resource as a guide while you meditate enables you to build up your safety skill set, empowering you to feel safe and protected in the emotions you are about to dive into. As you release stress hormones, they will present through sensations like shaking, heat, sweating, yawning, goosebumps, changed breath and gurgling in the stomach. Be curious about these feelings and sit with them. They will discharge all alone, naturally. Don't judge or critique anything you feel, or sense. Be present and continue to observe what happens next and experience the sensation of release from the body. Toward the end of this process, you might feel a bit calmer or have a great sense of release. Take a few minutes to lean into this, and expand the sense of calm. You will find strength in your body.

4 STAGES OF HEALING
your relationship with food

These are the stages I went through to heal my relationship with food. There are four stages of healing and for some people, the length of mastering one stage might feel longer than another depending on where the individual is on her/his journey.

MINDFUL EATING

Mindful eating is the practice of being more mindful and anchored in the present moment. It emphasizes the importance of focusing on the moment and being aware of thoughts, emotions, and senses while consuming food. By eating mindfully, you restore your attention and slow down, making eating an intentional act rather than an automatic one. What's more important is that, by increasing your recognition of physical hunger and fullness cues, you are able to distinguish between emotional and true physical hunger.

The purpose of mindful eating is not to lose weight, although it is highly likely that those who adopt this style of eating will lose weight. The intention is to help individuals savor the moment and the food and encourage their full presence for the eating experience.

Diets tend to focus on setting rules and keeping you in a box, while mindful eating focuses on bringing you back to the present moment and bringing awareness to all of your senses. All diets have the potential for success or failure based on weight outcomes. People may know their outcomes are going to depend on their consumption and expenditure of calories and understand that this has to do with their behavior, but it is rare for individuals to sustain behavior change without seeing results on their outcomes. Their behavior change will be subject to daily stress and outside pressures and therefore difficult to sustain.

Mindfulness is a process-oriented, rather than an outcome-driven, behavior. It is based on an individual's experience of the moment. The individual focuses on appreciating the experience of food and is not concerned with restricting intake. The person eating chooses what and how much to consume. It is not coincidental that, within a mindful approach, the person's choices often are to eat less, savor eating more, and select foods consistent with desirable health benefits. When I became a mindful eater I started to become mindful of my body, how food was impacting my body and cravings that were either connected to my physical microflora or my emotional state.

To start becoming more of a mindful eater, you

can start with this question, is it a craving or am I really hungry? We first need to understand the difference between a physical food craving—or actual hunger—and an emotional food craving. Cravings can be caused by either physical or psychological needs. Emotional cravings or eating triggers are usually caused by psychological needs, while hunger is a biological function of the body's real need for food. Emotional cravings can lead to binging. Learning to listen to your body and know what it is trying to tell you is a key step in ditching the diet and healing your relationship to food.

I'd like to offer you two scenarios, one from my personal experience and one from one of my client's personal experiences and journey together.

#1 Eating sadness in spoonfuls of Nutella

Nutella (aka sugar + a bit of cacao powder = deliciousness) was one of the hardest addictions to break for me. Not because of the lack of willpower to fight the cravings but because of the emotional attachment I had to childhood memories. I still vividly remember my mom and I's favorite things to make to boost our mood, was either bread and Nutella, crepes and Nutella, or, even better, indulging in spoonfuls of Nutella after a long day of work/school. This all happened in my parents' white Italian kitchen with brown cold tiles and a rectangular granite table, sitting on wooden chairs while trying to feel better about our feelings. But as I started working on healing myself and adopting more Ayurvedic practices, I realized that this behavior needed to stop. I couldn't continue to process

my feelings by eating nutella. I don't blame my mother for unconsciously teaching me how to cope with emotions, she was merely just passing down the best way she learned herself to survive her own childhood.

But one afternoon, while studying for a German test in my lavender colored bedroom, I decided to take a break and paused. In silence. Staring at the wall in front of me. My mind was fried but my spirit was about to tell me something. It was in that stillness, when I heard a voice that told me to start noticing my emotional response and to not react by grabbing the jar of Nutella but instead to stop and just observe the feeling without becoming it. This was the voice of my intuition starting to guide me through my healing journey with food and my body. The next step after acknowledging the feeling was to start focusing on healing the trigger and/or preventing that situation from happening. I began asking myself "what could I do instead? What would really nourish me at this moment?" Interestingly I started to come up with creative answers I never thought about before like "I need a nap", "I am stressed out about a school test", "I am feeling social anxiety at school", "I feel family pressure to be the good type A student that will carry the honor of the family".

The third step was to not judge what comes up but to remain in the feeling and explore it without attachments. That was when I started to separate my physical hunger from my emotional hunger.

#2 Drinking loneliness in a glass

I was shocked and excited to receive Susie's phone call on a warm May afternoon. A sweet, slim, blond hair, blue eyed, 60-year-old woman who spent her life fighting alcohol addiction through experiences in rehab and countless visits with different psychologists and psychiatrists. I guess the Universe thought I was ready to help a beautiful soul on the verge of death. When she came to me and said "I need help or I may die and I don't know what else to do", my whole body froze in chills. I knew that her trauma was the cause of her addiction, but she, like many of us, couldn't stop the reactive behavior of drinking a bottle of wine every night. So, we began our healing journey. The process was not linear or easy, but she had the courage to sit with her feelings, her wounds of abandonment from her mom, and her feelings of being the loneliest person on earth even with a supportive family and team by her side. Susie's journey was one of the most courageous healing journeys I've witnessed.

Adding in more mindfulness practices as well as doing some deep soul healing began to shift her life's trajectory. She started to be able to identify when her emotions were coming up. She began acknowledging these feelings without becoming the feelings. She began (over time) becoming more comfortable sitting with her emotions without trying to numb them. Without letting the feeling take over her. Slowly the dark cloud that dimmed her light for years started to lift. Now Susie has not relapsed for the past four months, the first time in 30+ years of her life.

MINDSET

This might be one of the most important skills you develop if you do it right. Remember, you can also apply it to all areas of your life.

Mindset is everything. It is the collection of beliefs and thoughts that make up the mental attitude, inclination, habit or disposition that predetermines a person's interpretations and responses to events, circumstances and situations

.

There are 3 steps in order for you to master your mindset around food.

1. **Set intentions, not goals.** This is something that I started doing with my clients. I stopped using the word "goals" since it felt very masculine, goal-driven and it embodies a very strong "pushy" energy. Instead, I started using the word "intentions" to define the roadmap that my clients would take to welcome a more gentle healing and feminine energy in their practice.

Think beyond "I want to lose x pounds" and go for a different feeling far beyond weight, such as:

- I want to heal my relationship with food

- I want to stop using food as a way of coping with my emotions

- I want to feel good in my body

- I want to create sustainable habits that fit

my lifestyle

2. **Focus on the journey.** An important factor when building a growth mindset in relation to healing your relationship with food is seeing the value in your journey. When you're fixated on the end result, you miss out on all the things you could be learning along the way. You miss out on the transformation that is happening within you. Be present with the person you are becoming. When you focus on the journey and you practice loving yourself along the way, that's when losing weight will be a byproduct of the work you do.

3. **Use powerful language.** Pay attention to your words and thoughts. Replace negative thoughts with more positive ones to build a positive mindset. One simple tool that changed my life has been keeping a gratitude journal. I learned that if you start having more gratitude and start writing it down, you start training your brain to find more things to be grateful about. You build the momentum.

Keeping a gratitude journal has helped my brain make an effort to look out for things I'm grateful for even in the face of adversity. It can be as specific or general as you wish it to be. You can start from thanking God or the Universe to thanking your job for all of the stability it provides in your life, or your clients, or your friends and family, etc.

GUT HEALTH

Your gut microbiome is the home base for the bacteria in your digestive tract. Here, they help you break down food and turn nutrients into things your body can use. We will talk more in-depth about gut health in the following chapter.

INTUITIVE EATING THROUGH AYURVEDA

As I shared in my previous chapter, the combination of my Italian background and my Ayurvedic studies helped me improve my relationship with food. Ayurveda had and still has a significant impact on my view of the world. After I studied it, I went through a period of intense activation. I don't look at people and/or food in the same way I used to. Ayurveda believes every living entity is made out of energy, and these days I read energies every day.

When I discovered my mind-body constitution, which I like to call my energetic blueprint, I learned the energetic properties of food. I started tuning in to the *medicinal and energetic effects* that different foods, herbs, and spices have on the physical, emotional and spiritual body.

True intuitive eating comes from knowing who you are, which means knowing your mind-body constitution, knowing the energies and properties of the food, and tuning into what foods and lifestyle practices will balance you that day and/ or that particular stage in life.

GUT HEALTH
your second brain

"All illness, as well as good health, begins in the gut and when your gut is suffering, there is a good chance that the rest of your health will, too."
~ Hippocrates

WELCOME TO GUT HEALTH: YOUR SECOND BRAIN

Honestly, I did not know this was one of the most important areas in the body until I started studying the mind-body connection and Ayurveda.

According to Ayurveda, your gut is your second brain and all diseases start here. Deepak Chopra, an alternative medicine advocate says, "All of the research that is coming out about well-being and how we maintain health shows that our gut health determines the health of everything in our body." Our gut does more than break down and digest food. It also breaks down and digests thoughts and processes emotions.

Because the enteric nervous system relies on the same type of neurons and neurotransmitters that are found in the central nervous system, some medical experts call the gut our "second brain." The "second brain" in our gut, in communication with the brain in our head, plays a key role in certain diseases in our bodies, as well as our overall mental health.

I remember finding this concept fascinating, so I started trying and testing things out. The first time I had pimples and a skin rash, not only did I apply herbal ointment, but I applied the Ayurvedic knowledge I was learning, as well. In two to four weeks, the rash started to disappear. When I developed a yeast infection (also known as candida) for the fifth time, I decided to do a dietary protocol called candida cleanse, which focused on gut health, and everything disappeared in a relatively short amount of time. When I started having acid reflux, dandruff, bloating, joint pain, and unfortunately, when I almost developed an autoimmune disease, I made that my wake-up call to treat my gut health consistently with respect and mindfulness.

And do you know why I am able to do this consistently? One of the most impactful elements of my childhood was watching my mom's poor health impact her and, as a result, my family's life. Before she had me, she survived thyroid cancer twice. By the time she had me, and throughout my childhood, she was always dependent on medications. She had heart problems, high blood pressure, and couldn't pick me up or participate in any lengthy outdoor activities with my brothers and I due to her severe back problems.

My mom was wonderful in so many ways and, looking back, she and my father worked together to compensate for each other's weaknesses with their strengths. I did all of the fun outdoor activities with my father. But you can imagine my apprehension and sadness as a child to see my mother's constant struggle with her health.

I remember promising myself that I would not end up walking the same health path. There are two things I want to share: one, find the WHY you want to get healthy, and two, focus on your gut health. It will save your life, as well as help you lose weight.

Your gut is the home base for the bacteria in your digestive tract, called the microbiome. Here, bacteria helps you break down food and turn nutrients into things your body can use. Bacteria stop growing when they run out of food, so you'll only have what you need.

Some microorganisms are harmful to our health, but many are incredibly beneficial and even necessary for a healthy body. Studies done by many organizations, including Harvard University over the past few decades, have found links between gut health and:

- the immune system
- mental health (anxiety, depression, etc.)
- autoimmune diseases
- endocrine disorders
- gastrointestinal disorders
- cardiovascular disease
- cancer

Microbiome and cravings

Microbes can increase our craving for foods they like by changing our taste buds through the production of neurotransmitters such as dopamine and serotonin that make us happy when these specific foods are consumed.

You may see cravings as just a sign of weak willpower, but your food preferences are tightly linked to your brain and, in particular, your mental state. There is a two-way communication pathway between the gut and brain via the vagus nerve. It is called the gut-brain axis. This connection is constantly implicated in research connecting diet and disease, including mental health conditions such as depression and anxiety.

This relationship starts with what we eat. For a long time, it has been known that what we eat can change the balance of microbes in our digestive tracts. What we consume can increase certain types of bacteria and diminish others – we'll talk more specifically about that shortly.

As bacterial populations change, they secrete different chemicals into our bodies. They also activate specific genes in our microbes that send out commands to the rest of the body including the brain, via the vagus nerve. This is how microbes are able to exercise control over our moods.

This "crosstalk" in communication between the brain and digestive system has opened up new ways to think about diseases. Not only do the gut and the brain communicate through the nervous system, but also through hormones and the immune system.

Digestive Fire

Ayurveda describes the biological fire of the body required for all metabolic functions (chemical processes for digestion of food) as 'Agni'. The food we eat is digested and absorbed from the stomach every day, which is important for maintaining life. Agni converts food into energy, which is responsible for all the vital processes of our body. Therefore, Ayurveda considers that Agni is the cause of life, complexion, strength, health, nourishment, teja (energy), oja (vitality) and prana (life energy).

The equilibrium of your digestive fire will impact the quality of your gut health and overall health. Let me start with an example.

Imagine that instead of your stomach, there was a fire. This fire is made up of 4 elements (also known as the fire tetrahedron): oxygen, heat, fuel and a chemical reaction. The important thing to remember is if you take any of these four things away, you will not have a fire, or your fire will be extinguished. Simple, right?

What happens when you add too much fuel (wood)? The fire does not breathe and it dies.

What happens when you pour water onto the fire? The fire weakens or dies.

What happens when the fire is weak and you add a non-quality type of log or a wet log? Smoke comes out.

Your digestion works the same way. If you eat too much food or the wrong kind of food for your mind-body constitution, your digestion will not work properly. Not only will you not be breaking food down properly, but this will also cause diseases like indigestion, malabsorption and the production of toxins in the body. These initial issues will cause bigger symptoms later on: leaky gut, weight gain, brain fog, joint pain, puffiness, poor sleep, mood swings, etc.

Remember, your digestive fire is the center of overall well-being—it's responsible for the digestion, absorption, assimilation, and transformation of food and sensations into energy.

GLUTEN/DAIRY FREE & BENEFITS

Why are the recipes in this book gluten and dairy-free? Am I not Italian?

Yes, I am 100% Italian, but just because I am, doesn't mean that I didn't change, research, and experience the power of healing my gut.

As I shared previously, the combination of bacteria that is found in our gut (our gut microbiome), not only aids our digestion but is also closely linked to our immune system. This is because these bacteria help to produce micronutrients (like vitamins and antioxidants) from the food we eat and break down carbohydrates, proteins, and fats to ease digestion. It is easy to see why we want our gut to function properly! And, the number one way to do this is through our diet.

There is a specific protocol to heal your gut; you can be as specific and strict as you want or need to be, depending on your level of care. Gluten and dairy can both cause long-term changes in your gut bacteria. Whether you have an intolerance to them or not, I recommend cleansing/taking a break once in a while, to let your cells regenerate.

What is Gluten?

Gluten is a protein found in grains, including wheat, rye, and barley. Gluten is naturally occurring, but it can be extracted, concentrated, and added to food and other products to add protein, texture, and flavor. It also works as a binding agent to hold processed foods together and give them shape. However, it is also the only protein found in food that is indigestible. The high amounts of gliadin prolamin (from gluten) and related prolamins (from wheat, barley, and rye) are **hard to digest** by human digestive enzymes (not just for those with gluten intolerance or Celiac disease).

Types of Gluten

Over the years, I have discovered that not many people know the different types of gluten, so I want to ensure you have this information. It's important to remember to read the ingredients in what you're planning to eat because even soy sauce contains gluten these days!

- Wheat
- Spelt
- Kamut
- Bulgar Wheat
- Triticale
- Durum
- Semolina
- Couscous
- Baley
- Pearl Barley
- Rye
- Einkom
- Emmer
- Farina

Pure oats can be eaten by most people with celiac disease, but make sure they are labeled gluten-free.

Gluten/Wheat Substitute

This book relies on several different flours, all found either in your local market, health food store, or national chain stores like Whole Foods or Amazon. Be sure to follow the guidelines provided in this book, as they will save you time in searching for products.

I want to bring to your attention a few products on the market that I love: coconut tortillas by Siete, found at Whole Foods, and gluten-free bread by Carbonaut, found at Sprouts. As for gluten-free flour mix options, I love Bob's Red Mill's gluten-free flour mix.

COOKING GUIDE FOR GRAINS

Preferably rinse and/or soak all grains for at least 30 minutes.

Quinoa

Rinse the quinoa. Pour the quinoa into a fine mesh colander and rinse under running water for at least 30 seconds. Drain well. This step removes any bitterness on the outside of the quinoa (caused by naturally occurring saponins). To cook 1 cup of dry quinoa add it to 2 cups of water or vegetable stock in a saucepan. Bring the mixture to a boil over medium-high heat, then decrease the heat a bit to maintain a gentle simmer. Cook until the quinoa has absorbed all of the liquid, about 10 to 20 minutes. This will yield about 3 ½ cups of cooked quinoa.

Basmati Rice

Place 1.5 cups of water and 1 cup of dry basmati rice in a saucepan. Bring to a simmer on medium-high heat and leave it uncovered. When the entire surface is bubbly and foamy, place the lid on, turn it down to medium-low and cook for 12 minutes until soft. Remove from the stove and let it rest for 10 minutes before serving.

Brown Rice

To prepare brown rice, rinse 1 cup of dry brown rice and drain, then add to a pan along with 2 cups of water or vegetable stock. Bring to a boil, then lower the heat to medium-low, cover, and simmer until the rice is soft, 45-50 minutes. Add a pinch of salt to the cooking water if you wish. This recipe will yield about 3 cups of rice.

Oats

There are different types of oats. Steel-cut oats will need to cook for about 45 minutes. To make 1 cup of dry steel-cut oats, add 3 cups of water and bring it to a boil. Lower the heat and simmer until done.

If you are using gluten-free rolled oats, place 2 cups of water in a pan and heat to a boil with 1 cup of rolled oats. Lower the heat and simmer until done, about 15 minutes.

If you are using gluten-free quick oats, place 1 cup of dry oats and 2 ½ cups of water in a pan. Bring water to a boil. Reduce heat to low, cover with lid and simmer until desired tenderness, 2-3 minutes. This will yield about 3 servings.

Polenta

Place 1 cup of polenta in a pan with 3 cups of water (if you like it softer, use 3 ½ cups of water) or milk/dairy-free milk and a pinch of salt. Bring to a boil, then lower the heat, cover, and cook for 20 to 25 minutes. This will make about 2 ½ cups.

Buckwheat

Place 1 cup of buckwheat groats into a fine-mesh strainer and rinse under cool running water until the water runs clear. Drain it well. In a small saucepan (covered with lid), bring 1 1/2 cups cold water and 1/2 teaspoon of fine salt to a boil over high heat. Bring it to a boil. Stir the buckwheat into boiled water and cover it with the lid. Bring back to a gentle simmer and reduce the heat to low. Cook until the water is absorbed, 13-15 minutes. Remove from heat and let the buckwheat rest covered for 10 minutes. This serving will make about 3 cups of cooked buckwheat.

Other Ingredients

Arrowroot and Cornstarch

I honestly use them both. For simplicity, I use cornstarch in my recipes. I don't have an allergy to corn. However, if you do, make sure that you use arrowroot instead.

If you use cornstarch, be sure to mix it in a small amount of liquid before adding it to your sauce, as it can develop clumps. Heat until it boils, then lower the heat and cook until thick. Arrowroot can be added ahead of time with a small amount of liquid to thicken a recipe or it can be added directly to the rest of the ingredients. It will thicken without lumps.

Baking Soda

Baking soda is a handy all-purpose item due to its wide variety of uses, from cleaning countertops and supporting oral care to baking.

Baking Powder

If you are concerned about the health risks of aluminum, you can buy aluminum-free baking powder in health food stores.

Nuts and Seeds

Nuts and seeds are so nutritious! They are rich in protein, healthy fats, and fiber. Most are also rich in minerals (such as magnesium, potassium, calcium, plant iron and zinc), vitamins B1, B2, B3, and vitamin E.

I always have nuts around the house. I frequently use almonds, cashews, and walnuts. Our favorite treat is pistachios and/or macadamia nuts. I am quite fond of pine nuts, as well, for my pesto recipe. I also love pumpkin seeds, sunflower seeds, and sesame seeds.

Chopped fine and/or roasted nuts and seeds make a crunchy topping for salad, yogurt or oatmeal and flavorful addition to steamed vegetables. However, If you have an allergy, read through a recipe's ingredients list before you begin preparing it.

Coconut Aminos

Coconut aminos have a milder, sweeter flavor, and less sodium than soy sauce. Soy sauce has a richer flavor and about three times as much sodium as coconut aminos. Coconut aminos are also gluten-free as they're made from the sap of the coconut palm, while soy sauce is traditionally made from fermented soybeans and wheat. In this book, I use coconut aminos for gluten-free purposes.

Dried Fruit

Dried fruit is highly nutritious. One piece of dried fruit contains about the same amount of nutrients as a piece of fresh fruit, but condensed in a much smaller package. Dried fruits can be eaten as a snack or they can be added to various dishes. In Indian cuisine, they are added to both sweet and savory dishes. They make the food rich and also bring a lot of flavor, aroma and texture to the dish.

Dates are not only my favorite, but they are one serious candidate for the title of healthiest dried fruit, with high levels of iron, fiber, potassium, antioxidants, and more. Dates also have a low glycemic index, so they do not typically contribute to a spike in blood sugar.

What is Dairy?

Dairy products are mass-produced and are included as ingredients in many different foods. A simple definition of dairy is that it is any food made from the milk products of animals. The most common dairy products come from cows, goats, and sheep. Dairy foods contain two major forms of protein: whey and casein.

Most people with an allergy to milk have symptoms that appear when they are infants and outgrow as they get older. However, some people do not outgrow these symptoms and continue to be allergic as adults. The development of a lactose intolerance tends to increase with age. If you think that dairy has become an issue for you, it is important to give yourself a break from it, especially if you are eating it every day. Notice how this makes you feel and go from there.

Milk

The base form in dairy products is taken from any lactating animal; this is the starting point.

Cream

This is created through processing milk; it involves the separation of fat from the milk and is often done using centrifugal force. Once the fat has been separated, it leaves a thick cream that contains high levels of butterfat. This is then pasteurized to kill off bacteria. The different varieties of cream are defined by their fat-to-butterfat ratio.

Butter

To make butter, the separation of fat from butter fat during the production of cream is continued. Whisking or centrifugal force is continued until the buttermilk separates. In mass production, additives such as salt are mixed in with the separation to add flavor and longevity.

Cheese

Cheese is made by taking milk and coagulating the casein, one of the proteins it contains. Casein is a very common protein in cow's milk and accounts for at least 80% of the proteins in it. The process is artificially sped up by first acidifying the milk, then adding an enzyme called rennet to the casein.

Yogurt

Yogurt is made using either milk or cream, which is then fermented in lactic bacteria. The fermentation breaks up the compounds in milk, so the bacteria can convert milk sugar into lactic acid. This is usually done through incubation and leads to a thickening of the milk or cream. It is also the reason for the slight tangy taste in some yogurts. Additives such as sugar, flavorings, fruit and preservatives are then used to provide variety.

Alternatives

Now that you have an idea of the different types of gluten and dairy, let's talk about how to healthily and mindfully integrate different options into your diet.

Being gluten and dairy-free sounds more complicated than it is. First of all, remember to read the ingredients on food labels. Second of all, start making a few changes in your kitchen pantry.

Milk Alternatives

You can choose between various milk alternatives these days, such as; soy, almond, oat, rice, hemp, coconut, and walnut milk. In many of my recipes, I use either almond or cashew milk.

Plant-based Butter

There are good replacements for butter these days. I mainly use two options:

Earth Balance brand is great for baking and desserts. Their shortening is vegan, non-GMO, trans-fat-free, dairy-free, and gluten-free.

Ghee

It's not dairy-free, though ghee is a great choice for people who are lactose-intolerant. My favorite brand is Ancient Organics. Ghee is the foundation of Indian cooking. It is cow's butter that has been heated low and slow, then strained, to remove caseins and whey, which are all the milk solids. It's cooked a step further than clarified butter, which gives it a beautiful golden color, nutty flavor, and lovely fragrance.

Oils

There are several oils that I would recommend, but my three favorites are extra virgin olive oil, avocado oil, and coconut oil. Both extra virgin olive oil and avocado oil are considered good fats and are excellent sources of monounsaturated fatty acids, which can help improve heart health. Extra virgin olive oil is slightly more nutritious though because it contains more potassium, calcium, iron, and vitamins. Coconut oil has many nutrients that contribute to your health and a good diet. It's full of fatty acids that your body needs and may help improve cognitive function, metabolism, and hair and skin health.

Sugar and Sugar Alternatives

Staying with the idea of both health and wellness, I made most of the recipes in this book using healthy alternatives to cane sugar like maple syrup, agave, and coconut sugar. You can get creative and use other alternative sweeteners like brown rice syrup, molasses, turbinado sugar, agave nectar, monk fruit sweetener, and stevia. I make most of my recipes with alternative sweeteners because they have a low rating on the glycemic index scale, lessen my kids' temper tantrums, and improve mood (less hangry!)

I did keep some dessert recipes using cane sugar to honor my Italian culture. If I start using maple syrup in tiramisù, it will change the traditional taste of the Italian recipe. I also wanted to give you an idea of balance. Balance is key. My motto is " 80% clean eating, 20% fun eating."

Adaptogenic Herbs & Superfoods

Adaptogens are herbal pharmaceuticals. They work to counteract the effects of stress in the body. Stress causes very real physical changes in the body, including harming the neurological, endocrine, and immune systems. This health cookbook contains recipes made with adaptogens and superfoods due to the stimulant properties that help counteract those harmful effects.

Some of my favorites are:

Maca

Classified as both an adaptogen and a superfood, maca is a root vegetable used by natives of the high Peruvian Andes for centuries to boost energy and libido. It's also revered for its ability to provide hormonal balance, reducing stress and anxiety.

Ashwagandha (Indian ginseng)

Traditionally used as an adaptogen, contains chemicals that might help calm the brain, reduce swelling, lower blood pressure, and alter the immune system.

Shatavari

Traditionally referred to as the "queen of herbs," shatavari supports and nourishes the entire body while restoring depleted vitality stores. It also promotes fertility and restores essential reproductive functions.

Spirulina

Spirulina is a blue-green algae, rich in nutrients, some of which aren't found in the average daily vitamin. It contains significant amounts of calcium, niacin, potassium, magnesium, B vitamins, and iron. It is also a complete protein. Spirulina is alkalizing to the body, which boosts liver function, a necessary element while detoxing. Spirulina contains chlorophyll which is used for "detoxification" by helping remove toxins such as heavy metals and other pollutants from the blood.

A NOTE
about portions

How much should I eat? When is what I eat enough for my body?

Do I need to weigh my food? What if I am still hungry?

These are some of the questions I am most often asked in my coaching practice. You want an answer. I hear you. But here is what I have to say.

There is no right answer. I can only give you guidelines to follow.

According to the U.S. Department of Agriculture (USDA), plates should be divided into sections that represent daily dietary guidelines for recommended fruits, veggies, proteins, and grains.

Guess what? Italians don't do that. If you pay attention to what they eat, the majority of the time, (as someone who is 100% Italian) they have a balanced amount of carbs throughout the day and lots of fresh fruit and veggies. Protein and dairy all come second.

What I came to realize over the years is that there are no "right" portion guidelines to follow every day because some days your body is more hungry than others. I find myself eating oatmeal, a bowl of pasta, and a sandwich with soup one day, and the next day my body wants to have only veggies and protein. This is the art of being an Intuitive Eater.

What is the secret?

Here is my secret to unlocking the code of natural weight loss: when you eat gluten-free, dairy-free, whole foods, gut health-friendly foods, you can eat as much as you want and not gain weight. I eat more than when I was on a diet and I am at my healthiest weight without struggling.

"Make food choices that honor your health and taste buds while making you feel good. Remember that you don't have to eat a perfect diet to be healthy. You will not suddenly get a nutrient deficiency or gain weight from one snack, one meal, or one day of eating. It's what you eat consistently over time that matters. Progress, not perfection, is what counts."

Evelyn Tribole, Intuitive Eating: A Revolutionary Program That Works

Herbs and Spices Chart

Turmeric

Antibacterial, blood cleansing, regulates insulin levels, protects intestinal flora. It helps decrease inflammation. Tridoshic.

Ginger

Releases toxicity while boosting the metabolism. It is heating, it helps increase circulation and decrease nausea (not recommended for high pitta) Great for VATA, KAPHA.

Asafoetida

Treats bloating, indigestion, gas, and abdominal pain. A strong heating potency, fights candida, balance blood sugar and IBS. Great for VATA.

Cumin

Enhances digestion and nutrient assimilation. Treats flatulence, bloating and indigestion. Powerful kidney and liver tonic.

Coriander

Aids digestion, relieves intestinal gas, regulates bowels, stimulates appetite, diuretic. Great for PITTA.

Fennel

Treats indigestion, bloating, gas, nausea. Enhances digestion. Diuretic.

Cinnamon

A warming spice with sweet, pungent, and bitter flavors used to revive digestion. Good for VATA and KAPHA. Improves circulation and clears toxins around joints. Clears respiratory passages.

Cardamom

Stimulates digestion, increases nutrient absorption. Good for the respiratory tract and to clear urinary tract, bladder and kidneys.

Mustard Seeds

Anti-inflammatory, antiviral, and antibacterial heating properties.

Rosemary

Stimulates hair growth, boosts mental activity, relieves respiratory problems, and reduces pain. Rosemary oil is used for hair care in shampoos and lotions. Regular use of rosemary oil helps to stimulate follicles, making hair grow longer and stronger.

Sage

Antifungal, astringent. It is added in gargles or mouthwash to clear any infection and respiratory tract. Sage helps provide better brain function and can be effective for symptoms of menopause, night sweats, and hot flashes.

Basil

Maintains and promotes the long-term health of the respiratory tract. Basil tea can help clear mucus from the lungs and the respiratory area. Settles stomach disorders and enhances digestion. A mild natural sleep aid, basil enhances the quality of sleep.

Easy Meal Plan

#1 Ignite your Digestion

Before drinking water in the morning, use a tongue scraper (stainless steel or copper) to remove any coating (bacteria) present on the tongue. Stick your tongue out and allow it to be loose and heavy. Work the tongue scraper back to front at least five times, rinsing the scraper after each round.

After step 1, upon rising, hydrate yourself before anything else. Drink 6-8 oz of warm or room temperature water, and add a squeeze of fresh organic lemon. Drinking lemon water in the morning provides a gentle flush for the whole system while also stimulating peristalsis- the wave-like movements occurring in your digestive tract. This beverage activates the digestive system (digestive fire) and purifies both the stomach and liver.

#2 Morning Routine

How you start your day is a good indicator of how the rest of it will pan out. So why not kick it off with some healthy balancing habits?

After hydration, I usually go back to the bathroom and finish getting ready by giving myself a body oil massage (at least once per week) before showering, washing my face, rinsing my eyes with cool water, and brushing my teeth.

Then I head off to my favorite part of the day, which is "me time". Connecting with myself and my Spirit Guides has become one of the most important parts of my day because it keeps me grounded, positive, and energized throughout the day. My favorite morning routine consists of meditation, setting intentions for the day, light stretching, journaling, maybe dancing, and pulling my daily oracle cards.

I encourage you to create your favorite morning practice that works for you and your schedule. And let's have a real mom talk! Every day might be slightly different, especially when you have kids. Do not get frustrated or try to force it if it doesn't flow when you first get up. The important part is for you to commit to it at some point in the morning so that you can keep yourself balanced for you and your family's mental sanity. And remember, if I can do it as a single mama entrepreneur, you can do it too!

#3 Breakfast

According to Ayurveda, warm breakfast in the morning is important to prepare the body for digesting the biggest meal of the day - lunch. Try to reduce as much as possible the intake of cold cereal and milk first thing in the morning as it is very congesting for the digestive system.

#4 Lunch

Lunch is considered the most important meal of the day in terms of the digestion process, according to Ayurveda and Italian Culture.

The ancient medical practice considers the Sun as the source of our metabolism and because it shines the brightest between 12 to 2 pm, this is considered the ideal time to have lunch. This is the time to have a mix of carbs, protein, and veggies. In Italy, it's the time of day when we eat a bowl of pasta, risotto, gnocchi, and ravioli with a side dish. Remember it has to fuel you for the rest of the day.

#5 Dinner

Dinner is the last meal of the day, so it should be a lighter meal to prepare you for a good night of sleep. Yet what I've noticed from living in the US is that there is an emotional component attached to dinner. Dinner is the time for family get-togethers, social life, and parties. It is the time we need to pay more attention because If we overeat or indulge in too many heavy foods, it will create ama (toxicity)

in the body. It's best to choose lean protein and sauteed, cooked veggies, soups, and sometimes salads.

#6 Evening Routine

After dinner, favor low-key and relaxing activities: take a leisurely walk, read a book, listen to relaxing music, draw or color, watch a light-hearted movie, etc. Computers/electronics, social media, or watching the nightly news can stimulate your mind and actually cause stress, so make sure you turn off any electronic device at least 30 minutes before going to bed. Cortisol, the stress hormone, is antagonistic to melatonin, the relaxation hormone and also the hormone associated with sleep. When cortisol goes up, melatonin goes down, which can be a problem because you may not be able to stay asleep at night.

	BREAKFAST	LUNCH	SNACK	DINNER
DAY 1	Oatmeal (p 225)	Black Bean Tacos (p 166)	Fruit	Broccoli Shrimp Curry (p 155)
DAY 2	Avocado Egg Toast (p 222)	Buddha Bowl (p 157)	Fruit	Salmon with Spicy Mango Salsa (p 172)
DAY 3	Tofu Scramble (p 221)	Kitchari (p 161)	Chia Seed Pudding of Your Choice (p 209)	Cauliflower Soup (p 120) + Chickpea Flatbread Farinata (p 91) & Italian Antipasto (p 95)
DAY 4	Berry Chia Yogurt Parfait (p 226)	Summer Pasta Salad (p 141)	Carrots + Homemade Hummus (p 93)	Lemon Sage Chicken Bites (p 171) + Grilled Veggies (p 116)
DAY 5	Oatmeal (p 225)	Collard Green-Rainbow Wrap (p 169)	Fruit	Pizza (p 149)
DAY 6	Smoothie of Your Choice (p 231)	Lasagna (p 142) + Cucumber Salad (p 129)	Avocado Chocolate Mousse (p 217)	Minestrone Soup (p 121)
DAY 7	Pancakes (p 229) or Waffles (p 227)	Fettuccine Alfredo (p 151) + Cucumber Salad (p 129)	Carrots + Homemade Hummus (p 93)	Chickpea Tikka Masala (p 160)

Antipasti
& KITCHEN STAPLES

Dressings

ALMOND BUTTER TURMERIC

INGREDIENTI

¼ cup almond butter
1 cup water
2 lemons, juiced
1 inch fresh ginger
2 tsp turmeric
2 tbsp maple syrup
1 tsp salt
¼ tsp black pepper

PREPARAZIONE

1. In a blender, combine all the ingredients and blend until smooth. Refrigerate in an airtight container for up to 7 days.

CREAM AVOCADO CILANTRO

INGREDIENTI

2 small avocado
2 limes, juiced
½ cup dairy-free milk
½ cup water
1 ½ tbsp garlic powder
1 tsp salt
½ tsp cumin
¼ cup cilantro

PREPARAZIONE

1. In a blender, combine all the ingredients and blend until smooth. Refrigerate in an airtight container for up to 7 days.

SESAME GINGER MISO

INGREDIENTI

⅓ cup tahini
2 tbsp apple cider vinegar
3 tbsp coconut aminos
⅓ cup water
1 tbsp mustard (dijon)
1 tbsp sesame oil
⅛ tsp cayenne pepper
½ inch fresh ginger
1 tsp organic mellow white miso

PREPARAZIONE

1. In a blender, combine all the ingredients and blend until smooth. Refrigerate in an airtight container for up to 7 days.

ITALIAN

INGREDIENTI

¼ cup balsamic
¾ cup extra virgin olive oil
1 garlic clove
2 tbsp honey
1 tsp salt
¼ tsp pepper
1 rosemary sprig

PREPARAZIONE

1. In a small bowl, whisk together the ingredients. Taste and adjust seasoning as desired. Refrigerate in an airtight container for up to 7 days.

Note. Contrary to its name, Italian salad dressing is not an Italian creation, but an American pantry staple inspired by Italian ingredients. The main reason why Italians don't buy any bottled dressing is that there is only one really popular salad dressing – a simple mix of oil and vinegar, plus salt.

HOMEMADE GLUTEN-FREE
bread

SERVINGS: 1 LOAF

PREP TIME: 15 MINS

REST TIME: 1 HOUR

COOK TIME: 30-45 MINS

TOTAL TIME: 2 HOURS

INGREDIENTI

2 ½ cups all-purpose gluten-free flour*

1 tsp xanthan gum; leave out if your flour already has it in it

1 tsp gluten-free baking powder

1 packet rapid rise/instant yeast

¼ cup extra virgin extra virgin olive oil

1 tbsp maple syrup

1 tsp apple cider vinegar

1 ½ cups warm water (100-110˚F)

3 egg whites, from large eggs and room temperature

1 tsp salt

NOTES

I like Bob's Red Mill 1-1 gluten-free flour mix. Not all gluten-free flours are created equal. You may experience different baking results depending on the gluten-free flour blend you choose.

PREPARAZIONE

1. Spray a 9x5 inch bread pan or a 9x4 inch small loaf pan with gluten-free cooking spray. Move the top oven rack to the middle rack.

2. Beat egg whites first for about 3 minutes until stiff. Set aside.

3. Meanwhile, add the gluten-free flour, baking powder, and instant yeast to a large bowl and stir to combine the ingredients.

4. Add the extra virgin olive oil, maple syrup, apple cider vinegar, salt, and warm water to the flour mixture and mix on low for 1 minute. If you are using a stand-up mixer, use the paddle attachment, not the dough hook.

5. Add stiff egg whites gently by hand into the mixture. The dough will look like a thick cake batter.

6. Pour the dough into a greased 9x5 inch bread pan or a 9x4 inch small loaf pan. Cover the pan with a kitchen towel and allow the bread to rise in a warm place for 1 hour.

7. Preheat your oven to 350°F.

8. Place in the oven to bake for 30-40 minutes at 350°F. Bake the bread on the middle rack horizontally. Check with a toothpick to see if it is ready. When the toothpick comes out dry, the bread is ready.

9. Allow the loaf to cool for 10 minutes in the pan. Remove the loaf from the baking pan and place it on a cooling rack. If the bread completely cools in the pan, the steam can get trapped and the loaf can get soggy, especially on the bottom. Allow the bread to cool completely before slicing.

10. Store the leftover bread in an airtight container in the fridge, once it's completely cooled. It may be kept on the counter at room temperature. It is also best not to pre-slice the bread before you store it, so just store the left-over portion of the loaf.

11. The bread can be frozen once it is completely cooled. Wrap the loaf tightly in plastic wrap, then wrap it in foil or freezer paper. Place the wrapped loaf in a freezer bag. The bread can be frozen for up to 3 months.

Homemade Gluten-Free Bread (p 88) | Homemade Hummus (p 93)

Homemade Pesto (p 92) | Chickpea Flatbread Farinata (p 91)

CHICKPEA FLATBREAD
farinata

SERVINGS: 8

PREP TIME: 5 MINS

SOAKING TIME: 1 HOUR

COOK TIME: 10 MINS

TOTAL TIME:
1 HOUR 15 MINS

INGREDIENTI

1 cup chickpea flour

½ tsp pink Himalayan salt

1/4 tsp freshly ground black pepper

1 ¼ cups lukewarm water

3 tbsp extra virgin extra virgin olive oil (plus 1 tbsp for the pan)

2 tsp fresh rosemary

PREPARAZIONE

1. In a large bowl, sift chickpea flour, salt, and pepper. Whisk in warm water and extra virgin olive oil. Let sit, covered with a cloth, for at least one hour.

2. Place your skillet in the oven and preheat to 450°F.

3. Once preheated, carefully remove your skillet from the oven and add a tablespoon of extra virgin olive oil – it will sizzle a bit. Immediately, pour your batter in a steady stream until it reaches the edges of the pan. Top it with rosemary.

4. Bake for 8 minutes until the edges are set. Then, turn on your broiler, and broil for 1-2 minutes. Keep your eyes on the flatbread: the top should turn dark brown very quickly, but make sure not to overdo it.

5. Remove the socca (flatbread) from the oven. With your hands, or with a small knife, cut into wedges. Sprinkle some salt and pepper, and serve immediately.

HOMEMADE PESTO

SERVINGS: 1 CUP

PREP TIME: 5 MINS

COOK TIME: 1 MIN

TOTAL TIME: 6 MINS

INGREDIENTI

2 ½ full cups basil leaves (remove big stems)

⅓ cup pine nuts

4 tbsp nutritional yeast

8 tbsp extra virgin olive oil

2 garlic cloves, *optional

Salt to taste

PREPARAZIONE

1. Combine basil leaves, pine nuts, nutritional yeast, extra virgin olive oil, and garlic (if you choose to use it) in a food processor and process until very finely minced.

2. Use it immediately, or store it in the refrigerator for up to 7 days, or freezer for up to 3 months.

HOMEMADE HUMMUS

SERVINGS: 1 CUP

PREP TIME: 5 MINS

COOK TIME: 1 MIN

TOTAL TIME: 6 MINS

INGREDIENTI

1 can chickpeas, drained and rinsed

¼ cup tahini

¼ cup fresh lemon juice

1 garlic clove

2 tbsp extra virgin olive oil

½ tsp cumin

½ tsp salt

2-3 tbsp water

Pinch of paprika for serving

PREPARAZIONE

1. In the bowl of a food processor or high-speed blender, combine all the ingredients.

2. Blend for 1 minute, scrape the sides and bottom of the bowl, then blend until smooth and creamy. Store it in the fridge for up to 5 days.

ITALIAN ANTIPASTO
platter

INGREDIENTI

1 ½ lbs assorted cured meats such as salami, prosciutto, pepperoni and coppa

Vegan Mozzarella Cheese Balls (p 100)

Ricotta (p 99)

Organic grapes

Fresh herbs to garnish

PREPARAZIONE

1. Arrange all the ingredients on a large platter. If using the sauces, place them in small bowls. Garnish with fresh herbs, then serve.

2. If you want to make this dish ahead of time, assemble everything on the platter except the bread products and fresh herbs. Cover and refrigerate for up to 8 hours. Remove from the refrigerator, uncover, and add bread and herbs. Let stand for 5-10 minutes, then serve.

NOTES

Feel free to add olives, nuts, figs, or grilled veggies to the platter.

Grilled Zucchini Rolls (p 97)

Smoked Salmon Avocado Crostini (p 98)

GRILLED ZUCCHINI
rolls

SERVINGS: 12

PREP TIME: 15 MINS

COOK TIME: 15 MINS

TOTAL TIME: 30 MINS

INGREDIENTI

2 medium zucchini, sliced thinly lengthwise

Oil for grilling

Plant-based cream cheese or Ricotta (p 99)

12 small sun-dried tomatoes

12 basil leaves

PREPARAZIONE

1. Brush the zucchini slices lightly with oil, and grill over medium-high heat until just tender, about 2 minutes per side, and set aside to cool.

2. Spread cream cheese over the zucchini slices.

3. Place a leaf of basil and half a sun-dried tomato on each slice of zucchini and roll them up.

4. Secure with a toothpick.

5. Plate and serve!

SMOKED SALMON
avocado crostini

SERVINGS: 6

PREP TIME: 5 MINS

COOK TIME: 10 MINS

TOTAL TIME: 15 MINS

INGREDIENTI

1 small garlic clove, minced *optional

1 avocado

1 tbsp lemon juice

¼ tsp sea salt

Pepper to taste

3–5 oz smoked salmon

Chickpea Flatbread Farinita (p 91)*

PREPARAZIONE

1. Prepare the chickpea flatbread according to the instructions.

2. Add garlic, avocado, lemon juice, salt, and pepper to a bowl and smash it with a fork.

3. Spread the avocado mixture over crostini, top with salmon, and serve.

NOTES
You can make crostini by toasting your favorite gluten-free bread in the oven if you do not want to make chickpea flatbread.

RICOTTA

SERVINGS: 1 CUP

PREP TIME: 5 MINS

SOAKING TIME: 1 HOUR

COOK TIME: 10 MINS

TOTAL TIME:
1 HOUR 15 MINS

INGREDIENTI

4 cups soy milk, I recommend one without sugar to have ricotta with a neutral taste*

1 tsp salt

2 ½ tbsp apple cider vinegar or white vinegar, or 4 tbsp of lemon juice

PREPARAZIONE

1. Put the soy milk into a large pot and bring it to a boil while stirring. Turn the heat off as soon as the milk boils, then add the salt and vinegar.

2. Stir with a spoon for 1 minute, then set aside for 10 minutes. During this time you should be able to see the soy milk curdle.

3. In the meantime, place a strainer onto a large bowl or pot. Cover the strainer with a clean kitchen cloth, made of cotton and with a fine mesh (or a cheesecloth).

4. After 10 minutes, pour the curdled soy milk into the strainer.

5. Now wrap the curdled milk in the cloth, put a weight on top (like a bowl filled with water) and let it drain for about 15-30 minutes.

6. After draining, the ricotta is ready to be used for both sweet (such as cannoli or pies) and savory (such as lasagna, ravioli with spinach, cannelloni, or stuffed shells) dishes.

NOTES

For best visual results, use a ricotta cheese mold that you can purchase online. The ricotta will have the same shape as the one in cheese stores.

VEGAN MOZZARELLA
cheese balls

SERVINGS: 14-18

PREP TIME: 10 MINS

COOK TIME: 20 MINS

TOTAL TIME: 30 MINS

INGREDIENTI

1 cup raw cashews, soaked

1 cup water

2 tbsp nutritional yeast

1 tsp salt

1 tbsp lemon juice

1 tbsp cornstarch

1 tbsp agar agar

½ cup water

Preparazione

1. Soak the cashews for at least 1 hour. Drain and rinse cashews.

2. Add the drained cashews, 1 cup of water, nutritional yeast, salt, lemon juice, and cornstarch in a high-speed blender. Blend until creamy. Set aside.

3. Pour ½ cup of water into a saucepan. Add agar agar and stir to combine until it is completely dissolved.

4. Add cashew mixture to the saucepan and stir to combine. Cook the mixture for about 5 minutes, constantly stirring, until it gets very thick and stretchy. Set aside for 5 minutes to cool down.

5. Prepare a large bowl of ice-cold water. Use a melon-baller to scoop out mini mozzarella balls, then carefully transfer them into the ice water.

6. Let the mozzarella balls sit in the ice water for a while (about 5 minutes) until the mozzarella has set. Then place the balls in an airtight container and cover them with salted water. Store in the fridge for up to 1 week.

VEGAN PARMESAN
cheese

SERVINGS: 12 OZ

PREP TIME: 5 MINS

TOTAL TIME: 5 MINS

INGREDIENTI

1 cup raw cashews

1/2 cup nutritional yeast

1 tbsp organic mellow white miso

½ tsp salt

Preparazione

1. Combine all of the ingredients in a food processor fitted with the "S" blade.

2. Pulse until a fine meal forms. Store covered in the refrigerator for up to 2 weeks.

BASIC TOMATO SAUCE

SERVINGS: 2

PREP TIME: 10 MINS

COOK TIME: 15 MINS

TOTAL TIME: 25 MINS

INGREDIENTI

28 oz passata di pomodoro or crushed fire-roasted tomatoes

¼ cup yellow onion, finely chopped

1 big garlic clove, minced

3 tbsp extra virgin olive oil

1 tsp salt

½ tsp turmeric

½ tsp sugar (cane or monk fruit sugar)

Pepper to taste

Fresh basil leaves

PREPARAZIONE

1. Heat extra virgin olive oil in a large wide skillet on medium heat. Add the chopped onion and garlic. Stir to coat. Reduce the heat to low, cover the skillet and cook for 3-5 minutes until golden.

2. Remove the cover and add the minced garlic. Increase the heat to medium-high. Cook garlic for 30 seconds.

3. Add the canned whole tomatoes.

4. Bring to a low simmer, reduce the heat to low, and cook, uncovered until thickened, about 15 minutes.

You can also make it into...

ARRABBIATA SAUCE

Add ½-1 tbsp hot red-pepper flakes to the red sauce and follow the instructions.

EGGPLANT TOMATO SAUCE

1. To make the eggplant red sauce, add one finely cubed eggplant with onion and garlic. Cook until tender.

2. Add the canned whole tomatoes.

3. Bring to a low simmer, reduce the heat to low, and cook, uncovered until thickened, about 15 minutes.

ZUCCHINI TOMATO SAUCE

1. To make the zucchini tomato sauce, add 2 finely cubed zucchini with onion and garlic. Cook until tender.

2. Add the canned whole tomatoes.

3. Bring to a low simmer, reduce the heat to low, and cook, uncovered until thickened, about 15 minutes.

OLIVE & TUNA SAUCE

1. To make the olive tuna sauce, add 1/4 cup chopped Kalamata olives, 1 tbsp chopped fresh parsley and (2) 5 oz cans of tuna packed in water, drained of the sauce. Break up any chunks of tuna with a fork or wooden spoon. Let simmer for 1 minute. Serve.

Immune-Boosting Adaptogenic Cauliflower Soup (p 120)

Soups, Salads
& SIDE DISHES

RATATOUILLE

SERVINGS: 4

PREP TIME: 15 MINS

COOK TIME: 45 MINS-1 HOUR

TOTAL TIME: 1 HOUR 15 MINS

You will need a 9-inch round pan

INGREDIENTI

1 eggplant

3 roma tomatoes

1 yellow squash

1 zucchini

Sauce

2 tbsp extra virgin olive oil

1 onion, diced

3 garlic cloves, minced

1 red bell pepper, diced

1 yellow bell pepper, diced

Salt, to taste

Pepper, to taste

28 oz can of crushed tomatoes

2 tbsp chopped fresh basil, from 8-10 leaves

Herb Seasoning

1 tsp garlic, minced

2 tbsp fresh parsley, chopped

2 tsp fresh thyme

Salt, to taste

Pepper, to taste

2 tbsp extra virgin olive oil

PREPARAZIONE

1. Preheat the oven to 375°F.

2. Slice the eggplant, tomatoes, squash, and zucchini into approximately $\frac{1}{16}$ inch rounds, then set aside.

3. Make the sauce: Heat the extra virgin olive oil in a 12-inch oven-safe pan over medium-high heat. Sauté the onion, garlic, red and yellow bell peppers until soft, about 10 minutes. Season with salt and pepper, then add the crushed tomatoes. Stir until the ingredients are fully incorporated. Remove from heat, then add the basil.

4. In a 9-inch round pan add half of the sauce in the pan, then smooth the surface of the sauce with a spatula. Arrange the sliced veggies in alternating patterns (for example, eggplant, tomato, squash, zucchini) on top of the sauce from the outer edge to the middle of the pan. Season with salt and pepper.

5. Make the herb seasoning: In a small bowl, mix together garlic, parsley, thyme, salt, pepper, and extra virgin olive oil. Spoon the herb seasoning over the vegetables.

6. Cover the pan with foil and bake for 40 minutes. Uncover, then bake for another 20 minutes, until the vegetables are softened.

7. Serve while hot.

NOTES

There will be leftover sauce. Store it in an air-tight storage container in the fridge for the next time you make yourself a pasta dish.

ZUCCHINI NOODLES
with romesco sauce

SERVINGS: 2

PREP TIME: 10 MINS

COOK TIME: 10 MINS

TOTAL TIME: 20 MINS

INGREDIENTI

12 medium zucchini

For the Sauce

2 tbsp of extra virgin olive oil

½ cup almonds, chopped

¼ cup small onion

1 garlic cloves, minced

1 tsp paprika

1 lb of tomatoes, seeded and chopped

1 tsp salt

½ tsp black pepper

1 tsp oregano, dry

PREPARAZIONE

1. Peel the zucchini with a regular peeler. Then, using a julienne peeler or spiralizer, make long slices along one side of each zucchini until you get down to the seeded core. Rotate the zucchini and continue to peel until you've done all four sides. Discard the core and set the noodles aside. (to avoid this process, buy zucchini noodles). Set aside.

2. Meanwhile, heat olive oil in a large skillet over medium-high heat. Add almonds and toast for 3 minutes, stirring often. Add onion, garlic, paprika, oregano, salt, pepper and cook.

3. Add tomatoes, mix the ingredients and cook for about 2 minutes.

4. Transfer the sauce mixture to a food processor or vitamix. Add the rest of the ingredients and blend on low speed until the sauce is smooth.

5. Add the zucchini noodles to the skillet, add 1 tbsp of water, cover, and steam until the zucchini is al dente in texture, 2-3 minutes.

6. Pour the desired amount of sauce over the cooked zucchini noodles.

7. Extra sauce can be stored into a glass storage container. Allow to cool before refrigerating. This sauce will keep for 5 days in the fridge.

ROASTED VEGGIES

SERVINGS: 4

PREP TIME: 10 MINS

COOK TIME: 30 - 45 MINS

TOTAL TIME: 40-55 MINS

INGREDIENTI

2 medium potatoes

1 medium carrot

1 medium parsnip

½ small kabocha squash*

1 small onion

3-4 garlic cloves, whole

½ tsp turmeric powder

½ tsp cumin powder

Pinch of cayenne pepper (optional)

2-3 tbsp extra virgin olive oil

½ tsp pink himalayan salt

⅛ tsp freshly ground pepper

Rosemary and thyme

NOTES
If not able to find kabocha squash, substitute with butternut squash.

PREPARAZIONE

1. Preheat the oven to 400°F. Lightly oil a baking sheet or coat it with nonstick spray.

2. Cut all the veggies into 1 inch pieces. Combine all of the veggies into a bowl. Add extra virgin olive oil, garlic, turmeric, cumin, cayenne pepper (if using), ground pepper, salt, thyme and rosemary. Gently toss to combine.

3. Place into the oven and bake for 30-45 minutes, or until tender. Serve immediately.

4. Serve warm or at room temperature.

SOUTH INDIAN
mashed potatoes

SERVINGS: 4

PREP TIME: 10 MINS

COOK TIME: 30 MINS

TOTAL TIME: 40 MINS

INGREDIENTI

2 lbs gold potatoes

½ cup ghee / extra virgin olive oil

1 tsp black mustard seeds

½ tsp fenugreek seeds

1 tsp curry powder

4 garlic cloves, chopped

3 small green Thai chiles or 1 serrano, halved

½ large yellow onion, chopped

½ cup frozen peas

1 tbsp ground coriander

1 tsp ground turmeric

1 (2 inch) piece of ginger, peeled and grated

½ tsp Kosher salt

Black pepper, to taste

⅓ cup cilantro, chopped

PREPARAZIONE

1. Peel, cut and cook potatoes in boiling water until just tender, 25–30 minutes; drain and set aside.

2. Heat oil (or ghee) in a 6 quart saucepan over medium-high. Cook onion and garlic first until golden.

3. Add mustard seeds and fenugreek seeds; cook for 1 minute until seeds start to pop. Then add curry powder, coriander, turmeric, ginger, salt and pepper.

4. Add potatoes, peas, and chiles. Uncover and stir, mashing lightly. Cook until slightly dry, 4–5 minutes. Stir in cilantro. Serve.

BACON BRUSSEL
sprouts

SERVINGS: 4

PREP TIME: 10 MINS

COOK TIME: 20-30 MINS

TOTAL TIME: 30-40 MINS

INGREDIENTI

1 ½ lbs brussel sprouts, trimmed and cut in half lengthwise

6 strips thick-cut bacon

1 tbsp extra virgin olive oil

1 tbsp maple syrup

¾ tsp salt

½ tsp black pepper

⅓ cup balsamic vinegar

PREPARAZIONE

1. Place a rack in the center of your oven and preheat the oven to 400˚F. For easy cleanup, line a large-rimmed baking sheet with parchment paper, and place the brussel sprouts in the center.

2. Drizzle with extra virgin olive oil, balsamic vinegar, and maple syrup, and sprinkle with salt and pepper. Gently mix until the brussel sprouts are evenly coated, then spread them into a single layer on the baking sheet.

3. Cut the bacon crosswise into ¼ inch pieces. Place bacon pieces evenly on top of the brussel sprouts.

4. Bake for 20-30 minutes, until the brussel sprouts are lightly charred and crisp on the outside and tender in the center and the bacon is crisp. Remove from the oven and serve immediately.

EASY SAUTÉED
zucchini

SERVINGS: 4

PREP TIME: 5 MINS

COOK TIME: 20 MINS

TOTAL TIME: 25 MINS

INGREDIENTI

4 medium zucchini

2 garlic cloves, minced

1 tbsp parsley, finely chopped

2 tbsp extra virgin olive oil

Pinch of black pepper

½ tsp salt

PREPARAZIONE

1. Wash and trim the zucchini, then dry them and cut them into slices approximately 1/8 inch thick.

2. Place the oil and garlic in a non-stick pan and sauté on medium-low heat until brown.

3. Add the zucchini with salt and pepper and cook for about 15-20 minutes until tender.

4. Top zucchini with parsley and serve. Enjoy!

TURMERIC ROASTED
cauliflower

SERVINGS: 4

PREP TIME: 5 MINS

COOK TIME: 25-30 MINS

TOTAL TIME: 30-40 MINS

INGREDIENTI

1 head of cauliflower

4-5 tbsp of extra virgin olive oil or avocado oil

½ tsp salt

2 tsp turmeric

¼ cup of nutritional yeast

Pepper to taste

PREPARAZIONE

1. Preheat the oven to 425°F.

2. In a large bowl, use your hands to coat the cauliflower florets with extra virgin olive oil, salt, pepper, turmeric, and nutritional yeast.

3. Transfer to a baking dish large enough to accommodate the florets in a single layer (such as a 9x13 inch rectangular baking dish).

4. Roast, stirring once, until browned and tender, 15-25 minutes.

5. Serve the roasted cauliflower immediately.

GARLIC SPINACH

SERVINGS: 4

PREP TIME: 2 MINS

COOK TIME: 5 MINS

TOTAL TIME: 7 MINS

INGREDIENTI

1 lb baby spinach leaves

1 tsp salt

1 tbsp fresh lemon juice

2 tbsp ghee or extra virgin olive oil

3 garlic cloves, whole and peeled

PREPARAZIONE

1. Add the extra virgin olive oil and garlic to a cold, large skillet and bring to medium heat. Cook until the garlic is fragrant and begins to caramelize, but watch it closely so it doesn't brown, or it will become bitter. Quickly remove the garlic from the oil.

2. Add the spinach in heaping batches, tossing in the oil as it reduces. Season with the kosher salt and freshly ground pepper and cook just until it wilts.

3. Add the garlic back to the spinach, toss, and drizzle with the lemon juice, and taste for seasoning. Serve hot.

SAUTÉED ASPARAGUS

SERVINGS: 3-4

PREP TIME: 5 MINS

COOK TIME: 10 MINS

TOTAL TIME: 15 MINS

INGREDIENTI

1 bunch of asparagus (about 1 ¼ lbs)

2 tbsp extra virgin olive oil or ghee

2 garlic cloves, chopped

1 tsp salt

½ tsp ground black pepper

2 tbsp Vegan Parmesan Cheese, for serving (p 101)

1/2 a lemon, juiced

PREPARAZIONE

1. Trim the woody ends from the base of the asparagus spears by cutting off the bottom 1 inch.

2. Heat a large skillet over medium-high heat. Add the oil and swirl to coat the pan. Add the asparagus in a single layer and cook, turning occasionally, until lightly golden and almost tender, 8-10 minutes. (Cut a small piece from the end of one asparagus to see if it's near tender.)

3. Reduce the heat to low. Add garlic, salt and pepper and stir to coat the asparagus. Cook until the garlic is softened and fragrant, 1-2 more minutes. Immediately transfer to a serving plate.

4. Just before serving, squeeze the lemon juice over the asparagus and sprinkle with vegan parmesan cheese. Serve immediately.

GRILLED VEGGIES

SERVINGS: 4

PREP TIME: 15 MINS

COOK TIME: 20 MINS

TOTAL TIME: 35 MINS

INGREDIENTI

2 zucchini

2 eggplant

2 red bell pepper

2 red onion

2-3 tbsp extra virgin olive oil

Salt, pepper and dried oregano to taste

PREPARAZIONE

1. Prepare the grill with clean grates and preheat to medium heat, 350°F to 450°F.

2. Trim the ends of the eggplants, zucchini, and onions and cut into 1/3 -1/2 inch slices. Seed the red bell pepper and cut into quarters.

3. Drizzle the vegetables with extra virgin olive oil and sprinkle evenly with salt and pepper. Grill the vegetables with the grill lid closed until tender and lightly charred all over, about 8-10 minutes for the bell peppers and onion; 5-7 minutes for zucchini and eggplant.

4. Serve warm or at room temperature.

BAKED SPAGHETTI
squash

SERVINGS: 2

PREP TIME: 10 MINS

COOK TIME: 35-40 MINS

TOTAL TIME: 50 MINS

INGREDIENTI

Small-medium (around 1 lb) spaghetti squash, halved lengthwise and seeded

1 tsp extra virgin olive oil

2 tbsp Vegan Parmesan Cheese (p 101)

4 Vegan Mozzarella Cheese Balls (p 100)

1 garlic clove, grated *optional

Dried oregano to sprinkle on top

Celtic sea salt and black pepper

1 tsp plant-based butter or ghee

PREPARAZIONE

1. Heat the oven to 450°F. Brush the cut side of each squash half with 1 tsp extra virgin olive oil.

2. Place squash, cut-sides down on a parchment-lined baking sheet and roast until the squash is tender when poked with a fork, 35-40 minutes.

3. Pull the squash out of the oven and flip it. Add two fresh Vegan Mozzarella Cheese Balls on each side, top it with grated garlic (if using it). Sprinkle oregano, Celtic sea salt, black pepper, vegan parmesan, and ½ tsp ghee or plant-based butter on each side.

4. Turn on the broiler. Roast for 2-4 minutes until the top is golden brown. Serve immediately!

IMMUNE-BOOSTING ADAPTOGENIC
cauliflower soup

SERVINGS: 4

PREP TIME: 10 MINS

COOK TIME: 10 MINS

TOTAL TIME: 20 MINS

INGREDIENTI

1 tbsp extra virgin olive oil or ghee

1 cup coconut milk

1 cup yellow onions, chopped

1 garlic clove, chopped

1 head of cauliflower, chopped

1 medium potato, peeled and chopped (about 4-5 oz)

4 cups unsalted vegetable broth

1 tsp sea salt

⅛ tsp fresh black pepper

1 tsp shatavari powder

1 tsp ashwagandha powder

1 tsp turmeric

1 lemon, juiced

Garnish with radishes slices, watercress or arugula and sunflower seeds.

PREPARAZIONE

1. Heat the extra virgin olive oil in a large pot set over medium heat. Saute the onion, garlic, turmeric, salt, and black pepper until soft.

2. Add the roasted cauliflower, potato, coconut milk, and vegetable broth and simmer for 5-10 minutes. Add the shatavari, ashwagandha, and lemon juice. Mix thoroughly.

3. Transfer to a high-speed blender. Puree on high until completely smooth. Add more salt and pepper to taste. Serve warm, garnished with sliced radishes, watercress or arugula, and sunflower seeds.

MINESTRONE SOUP

SERVINGS: 4

PREP TIME: 10 MINS

COOK TIME: 30 MINS

TOTAL TIME: 40 MINS

INGREDIENTI

2 medium potatoes, diced

2 medium carrots, peeled, quartered and sliced

1 stalk celery, diced

1 zucchini, diced

1 cup frozen peas

1 (15 oz) can pinto beans

1 (14-oz) can diced tomatoes

1 small yellow onion, finely chopped

2 garlic cloves, minced

1 tsp salt

¼ tsp pepper

¾ tsp turmeric

½ tsp cumin

1 fresh rosemary twig

2 tbsp extra virgin olive oil

4 cup vegetable broth

PREPARAZIONE

1. Heat the extra virgin olive oil in a large pot over medium-high heat. Add onion and garlic and saute until golden. Add salt, pepper, turmeric, cumin and stir for 30 seconds.

2. Add potatoes, carrots, celery, and zucchini to the pot and cook until the vegetables are tender, 5 -10 minutes.

3. Add the can of diced tomatoes, vegetable broth and rosemary twig to the pot. Simmer for 15 minutes.

4. Add frozen peas and pinto beans and simmer for a couple of minutes. Remove rosemary twig. Serve when it's ready.

GINGER BUTTERNUT
squash soup

SERVINGS: 4

PREP TIME: 10 MINS

COOK TIME: 30 MINS

TOTAL TIME: 40 MINS

NOTES

Buy the cubed and peeled butternut squash for a 10 minutes prep time.

INGREDIENTI

1 tbsp extra virgin olive oil or ghee

1 cup yellow onions, chopped

1 garlic clove, chopped

2 lbs butternut squash, cubed and peeled

1 small potato, peeled and cubed

1½ tsp grated fresh ginger or ½ tsp ginger powder

2 cups unsalted vegetable broth

¾ tsp sea salt

¼ tsp fresh black pepper

PREPARAZIONE

1. Heat the extra virgin olive oil (or ghee) in a large pot over medium heat. Add onion, garlic, salt, pepper, and ginger, and cook until softened, occasionally stirring, about 3-5 minutes.

2. Add cubed butternut squash and cubed potato to the pot and cook for about 8 minutes more, stirring occasionally.

3. Add 2 cups of broth, depending on your desired consistency. Reduce to a simmer, cover with a lid and cook until butternut squash is tender, about 10 minutes.

4. Let cool slightly and transfer to a blender. Blend until smooth. Taste and adjust seasonings.

5. Serve with parsley.

LENTIL AND SWEET
potato soup

SERVINGS: 4

PREP TIME: 10 MINS

COOK TIME: 30-40 MINS

TOTAL TIME: 50 MINS

INGREDIENTI

2 tbsp extra virgin olive oil

1 small onion, chopped

1 garlic clove, minced

1 cup green lentils, rinsed and soaked for at least 30 minutes

1 small sweet potato, peeled and cubed

½ cup celery, chopped

½ cup carrot, chopped

3 cups vegetable broth

1 bay leaf

¼ tsp black pepper

1 tsp sea salt

1 tbsp curry

1 can coconut milk

Fresh parsley, as garnish

PREPARAZIONE

1. In a large pot on medium-high heat, drizzle a little extra virgin olive oil and saute onion and garlic until fragrant, about 3 minutes.

2. Add curry powder, black pepper, and sea salt. Stir for 1 minute on low heat.

3. Add the rest of your ingredients, turn the heat up to high, and bring everything to a rapid boil.

4. Once it starts boiling, turn the heat down to a low simmer and cook uncovered for about 30-40 minutes, until lentils are cooked through but not falling apart.

5. Remove the soup from heat, and top with fresh parsley, serve and enjoy!

NOTES
Add more vegetable broth if needed.

TUSCAN PORTOBELLO
soup

SERVINGS: 4

PREP TIME: 10 MINS

COOK TIME: 15-20 MINS

TOTAL TIME: 25-30 MINS

INGREDIENTI

2 large portobello mushrooms, coarsely chopped

2 cans (15 oz each) cannellini beans, rinsed and drained

1 medium onion, chopped

2 garlic cloves, minced

2 medium carrots, diced

1 medium potato, diced

2 tbsp extra virgin olive oil

3 ½ cups vegetable broth

1 can (28 oz) diced tomatoes, undrained

2 cups fresh kale, chopped

1 bay leaf

1 tsp dried thyme

½ tsp dried basil

½ tsp dried rosemary, crushed

½ tsp salt

¼ tsp pepper

PREPARAZIONE

1. In a large skillet, heat extra virgin olive oil in a pan over medium-high. Cook onion and garlic until golden.

2. Add portobello mushrooms, thyme, dried basil, dried rosemary, salt, pepper and bay leaf.

3. Add broth, carrots, and potatoes. Bring to a boil. Cook until liquid is reduced by half.

4. Stir in the tomatoes, kale and cannellini beans. Bring to a boil. Reduce heat; cover and simmer for 8-10 minutes. Discard bay leaf and serve.

FENNEL AND
orange salad

SERVINGS: 4

PREP TIME: 10 MINS

TOTAL TIME: 10 MINS

INGREDIENTI

1 large fennel bulb, trimmed and thinly sliced

2 medium oranges, peeled

1 tbsp extra virgin olive oil

Salt and pepper

¼ cup pumpkin seeds

1 tbsp apple cider vinegar

¼ cup raisins

PREPARAZIONE

1. Place the sliced fennel in a salad bowl.
2. Slice the peeled oranges and divide them into flesh sections and add to the bowl.
3. Combine the extra virgin olive oil, apple cider vinegar, salt, and pepper to taste and drizzle over fennel and oranges. Top it with raisins and pumpkin seeds. Toss and serve.

Cucumber Salad (p 129)

Salmon With Blueberry Sauce (p 172)

CUCUMBER SALAD

SERVINGS: 2

PREP TIME: 10 MINS

TOTAL TIME: 20 MINS

INGREDIENTI

2 medium cucumbers, thinly sliced

¼ cup extra virgin olive oil

¼ cup cider or white vinegar

½ cup red onions, thinly sliced *optional

2 tbsp honey

¼ tsp black pepper

½ tsp salt

½ tsp dried dill

3 tbsp pomegranate seeds

PREPARAZIONE

1. In a medium bowl, toss the cucumber and onion slices, if using them.

2. In a large mixing bowl or Vitamix, whisk together oil, vinegar, salt, honey, dill, and black pepper.

3. Toss the dressing with the sliced cucumbers and green onions.

4. Refrigerate until ready to serve, and top with pomegranate seeds. Store the leftovers with their juices in an airtight container in the refrigerator for up to 3 days.

APPLE CRANBERRY PECAN
kale salad

SERVINGS: 2

PREP TIME: 10 MINS

TOTAL TIME: 20 MINS

INGREDIENTI

3 cups kale, chopped

½ cup dried cranberries

½ cup pecans, coarsely chopped

1 cup plant-based Ricotta, crumbled (p 99)

1 medium Granny Smith apple, chopped

1-2 tbsp fresh lemon juice

1 lemon zest

½ cup red onion, finely chopped *optional

Italian Dressing (p 87)

PREPARAZIONE

1. Start by slicing (or ripping by hand) the kale from the woody stalk in the middle of the kale leaf.

2. Next, rinse the kale in a colander or sieve. Use a salad spinner to remove the excess moisture or pat it with a paper towel.

3. Use a cutting board and roll up the kale lengthwise and chop it into smaller pieces. Place the kale in a large mixing bowl. Next, massage the kale with lemon juice. Yes - a quick 30-second kale massage is the secret to softening up the kale's texture.

4. Add in the dried cranberries, pecans, grated lemon zest, apple, plant-based Ricotta, and red onion, If using it.

5. Use a mason jar to make the Italian Dressing. Put the lid on and shake it vigorously for one minute. The dressing will emulsify into a delicious dressing ready to be poured onto the salad.

6. Pour the dressing onto the salad and toss the salad until the dressing is coating most of the leaves and other ingredients. Serve.

BLACK BEAN
and corn salad

SERVINGS: 3

PREP TIME: 10 MINS

TOTAL TIME: 15 MINS

INGREDIENTI

1 can black beans

1 cup corn kernels

2 tomatoes, chopped

½ avocado, cubed

1 green onion, chopped

½ cup cilantro, chopped

½ lime, juiced

¼ tsp salt

Pinch of pepper

1 tbsp extra virgin olive oil

1 tbsp hemp seeds

PREPARAZIONE

1. In a large bowl combine black beans, corn, tomatoes, avocado, green onion, and cilantro.

2. In a small bowl, combine the extra virgin olive oil, salt, pepper, lime and hemp seeds.

3. Pour over salad, toss and combine.

ARUGULA & PEAR
salad

SERVINGS: 2

PREP TIME: 10 MINS

TOTAL TIME: 20 MINS

INGREDIENTI

3 oz arugula (about 2 cups)

1 pear, thinly sliced

½ pecans

⅓ cup red onion, thinly sliced

Italian Dressing (p 87)

Vegan Parmesan Cheese (p 101)

PREPARAZIONE

1. Put the greens in a large bowl or on a platter. Top with the remaining ingredients.

2. Drizzle with 2 or 3 tbsp of the Italian Dressing and toss gently to coat. Sprinkle 2-3 tbsp Vegan Parmesan Cheese.

3. Serve the salad with additional dressing on the side, to taste.

SWEET POTATO &
kale salad

SERVINGS: 2

PREP TIME: 10 MINS

COOK TIME: 20 MINS

TOTAL TIME: 30 MINS

INGREDIENTI

4-5 kale leaves, chopped into small to mid-sized pieces

1 large sweet potato (about 1 lb), washed and cut into long wedges

1 tsp garam masala

2 tbsp extra virgin olive oil

½ tsp of salt

2 cups water

½-1 lemon, juiced

Pink Himalayan sea salt and black pepper

1 garlic clove, minced *optional

NOTES
For additional flavor, top your salad with avocado dressing (p 86)

PREPARAZIONE

1. Preheat the oven to 375˚F. Mix 1 tbsp extra virgin olive oil, garam masala, and salt with the potato wedges. Bake for 15-20 minutes.

2. While sweet potatoes are cooking, boil water. Add chopped kale to boiling water for 2 minutes. Drain the water quickly after the leaves become dark green.

3. In a bowl, add kale and lemon juice and massage well. Then add cooked sweet potatoes, mix well and sprinkle with pink Himalayan sea salt and black pepper, and remaining 1 tbsp extra virgin olive oil (and minced garlic if using) together. Serve hot.

SPICY PINEAPPLE
slaw

SERVINGS: 4

PREP TIME: 15 MINS

TOTAL TIME: 20 MINS

INGREDIENTI

2 cups cabbage

1 cup pineapple

1 medium carrot

½ cup cilantro

½ inch fresh ginger

1 tbsp of lemon zest (roughly one medium-sized lemon)

1 lime. juiced

2 tbsp extra virgin olive oil

1 serrano pepper, finely chopped *optional

PREPARAZIONE

1. Shred cabbage and carrots, chop cilantro, slice fresh ginger, grate lemon zest, and dice pineapple into bite-sized chunks.

2. Add all ingredients to a large salad bowl and toss thoroughly.

3. Combine the extra virgin olive oil and juice of lime. Drizzle on top before serving.

NOTES

Add finely chopped serrano pepper if choosing to use it in step #2.

Cannelloni Ricotta & Spinaci (p 144)

Main Dishes

SUMMER PASTA
salad

SERVINGS: 4

PREP TIME: 10 MINS

COOK TIME: 10 MINS

TOTAL TIME: 20 MINS

INGREDIENTI

2 ½ cups cherry tomatoes, cut in half

2 ½ cups spinach

1 small red onion, finely chopped

½ block tofu, drained and diced

⅓ cup sliced almonds

1 package of gluten-free pasta

¼ cup fresh basil

Dressing*

⅓ cup extra virgin olive oil

2 tbsp nutritional yeast

1 lemon, juiced

½ tsp salt

¼ tsp black pepper

PREPARAZIONE

1. Bring a large pot of salted water to a boil. Add the pasta and cook until al dente. Drain, then rinse with cold water to cool. Set aside.

2. In a small jar combine the extra virgin olive oil, nutritional yeast, lemon juice, salt and black pepper. Close the lid and shake it well. Set aside.

3. In a large bowl, combine pasta, spinach, tomatoes, red onions, basil, tofu, and almonds. Pour the dressing over the pasta salad and gently stir to combine. Chill until ready to serve.

NOTES
Or choose any one
of the Dressings (p 86)

LASAGNA

SERVINGS: 4

PREP TIME: 30 MINS

COOK TIME: 2.5 HRS

TOTAL TIME: 3 HRS

For The Bolognese Sauce

INGREDIENTI

2 (16 oz) organic beef packages (about 1 lb)

3 (14 oz) polpa crushed tomatoes (by Mutti)

1 celery stalk, finely chopped

1 medium onion, finely chopped

1 medium carrot, finely chopped

1 garlic clove, minced

½ cup red wine *optional

4 tbsp extra virgin olive oil

1 ½ -2 tsp salt

½ tsp pepper

2 rosemary twigs

PREPARAZIONE

1. Heat extra virgin olive oil in a large heavy pot over medium-high heat. Add onion, garlic, celery, and carrots. Sauté until soft.

2. Add beef and start breaking it up with a spatula or wooden spoon until browned, about 10 minutes

3. Add wine and rosemary and bring sauce to a boil. Simmer for 1 minute, stirring often until the wine has fully evaporated.

4. Add 3 cans of polpa (plain) and stir to blend. Reduce heat to very low and gently simmer, occasionally stirring until flavors meld, and cook for about 1 ½ hours. Season with salt and pepper. If it starts to be too dry then add some water. Set aside.

Besciamella
INGREDIENTI

4 cups unsweetened plain almond milk

3 tbsp cornstarch

½ cup ghee

½ tsp salt

¼ tsp nutmeg

PREPARAZIONE

1. In a medium pan, melt ghee at low heat, then add salt and nutmeg. When melted add the cornstarch and stir quickly.

2. Now add a little bit of (alternative) milk and make sure you stir so there are no flour clumps, then add the rest of the milk.

3. Keep stirring the milk at low-medium heat until it hardens at the desired consistency. Set aside.

FOR ASSEMBLING

Bolognese Sauce

Besciamella

2 packages of gluten-free lasagna sheets

1 cup Vegan Parmesan Cheese (p 101)

PREPARAZIONE

1. Preheat the oven to 375˚F.

2. To assemble, spread ½ cup (enough so lasagna sheets don't stick) of bolognese sauce in the bottom of a 9x13 inch baking dish. Arrange 6 noodles lengthwise on top.

3. Spread with more bolognese sauce. Top with besciamella sauce. Sprinkle ¼ cup Vegan Parmesan Cheese. Repeat layers one more time.

4. Bake for 25-30 minutes. Check it with a fork to make sure the noodles are cooked. Cool for 10 minutes before serving.

CANNELLONI RICOTTA
& spinaci

SERVINGS: 18

PREP TIME: 30 MINS

COOK TIME: 35 MINS

TOTAL TIME: 1 HR 5 MINS

Tofu Ricotta

INGREDIENTI

1 tbsp extra virgin olive oil

1 yellow onion, chopped

3 garlic cloves, minced

4 big handfuls fresh spinach

1 block (14 oz) extra-firm tofu, drained

¼ cup fresh lemon juice

4 tbsp Vegan Parmesan Cheese (p 101)

1 tbsp white miso paste

1 tsp salt

½ tsp black pepper

1 small bunch of fresh basil leaves

PREPARAZIONE

1. Heat the extra virgin olive oil in a skillet over medium-high heat. When hot, add in the onion and garlic, and sauté until the onion begins to soften but not brown, about 4 minutes.

2. Reduce the heat to low and add in the spinach, then cover. Check and stir the spinach every minute until the spinach has wilted, about another 4 minutes.

3. Break the tofu into four pieces and add it to a food processor (recommended) or blender. Add the sautéed onions, garlic, and spinach along with the remaining ingredients. Blend until smooth and creamy, stopping to scrape the sides as needed. If your ricotta is too thick, add 1-2 tbsp of water as needed to reach desired consistency.

4. Add in the basil, reserving some basil leaves for garnish. Pulse a couple of times, stopping to scrape the sides as needed until the ricotta is spotted with green throughout.

INGREDIENTI

1 batch Tofu Ricotta

5 cups jarred prepared tomato sauce

18 gluten-free fresh lasagna sheets

NOTES

I usually use the extra lasagna sheet to make pasta for another day.

PREPARAZIONE

1. Preheat your oven to 350°F.

2. Spread about ¼ of the tomato sauce in the bottom of a 9x13 inch pan. Grab one fresh gluten-free lasagna sheet. Scoop the ricotta mixture onto the top of the pasta sheet. Roll it halfway until the two ends of a sheet touch each other. *Cut and discard the extra part of the sheet.

3. Lay all the noodles in the baking dish with the sauce in a single layer. Repeat with the remaining noodles until the dish is full and the ricotta is used up.

4. Cover with the remaining tomato sauce making sure each noodle is coated in sauce.

5. Bake for 30-35 minutes until the cannelloni are tender and the sauce is hot. Remove from the oven and garnish with basil leaves.

EGGPLANT PARMESAN

SERVINGS: 4

PREP TIME: 15 MINS

COOK TIME: 20-30 MINS

TOTAL TIME: 45 MINS

Besciamella

INGREDIENTI

2 tbsp plant-based butter

2 cups almond milk (or milk of your choice)

3 tbsp cornstarch

¼ tsp nutmeg

pinch of pepper

salt to taste

PREPARAZIONE

1. In a medium pan, melt the plant-based butter at low heat, add salt, and nutmeg, pepper, and when melted, add the cornstarch and stir quickly.

2. Now add a little bit of milk and make sure you stir, so there are no flour clumps. Then add the rest of the milk.

3. Keep stirring the alternative milk at low-medium heat until it hardens to the desired consistency.

INGREDIENTI

1 large eggplant, thinly sliced

2 tbsp extra virgin olive oil

1 garlic clove, minced

½ small yellow onion, finely chopped

½ tsp salt

¼ tsp pepper

½ tsp sugar

4-6 basil leaves

17 oz plain tomato sauce (passata di pomodoro)

Vegan Parmesan Cheese (p 101)

Besciamella (p 146)

PREPARAZIONE

1. Slice eggplant: remove the stem from the eggplant, then cut it into thin slices.

2. Grill eggplant slices in a hot cast iron pan for about 2 minutes on each side. Set aside.

3. Meanwhile, prepare the tomato sauce. Heat the extra virgin olive oil in a large pot over medium-high heat. Add onion and garlic and saute until golden. Add salt, pepper, and sugar and stir for 30 seconds.

4. Add tomato sauce and basil leaves and cook for 5 minutes. Set aside.

5. Preheat the oven to 375˚F.

6. Assemble: in an 8x11 inch casserole dish, spread a layer of tomato sauce on the bottom. Then layer: eggplant slices, spoonfuls of tomato sauce, spoonfuls of besciamella and Vegan Parmesan Cheese.. Repeat an additional layer on top.

7. Bake for 20 minutes.

8. After 20 minutes, broil for 2 minutes and serve.

PIZZA

SERVINGS: 1 PIZZA

PREP TIME: 10 MINS

COOK TIME: 15 MINS

TOTAL TIME: 25 MINS

INGREDIENTI

2 cups gluten-free flour

1 tsp baking powder

½ cup warm temperature water

1 tsp maple syrup

1 tsp salt

2 tbsp extra virgin olive oil

Basic Tomato Sauce (p 102)

Vegan Mozzarella Cheese Balls (p 100)

PREPARAZIONE

1. In a bowl combine the flour, baking powder, maple syrup, yeast, and salt. Mix well.

2. Stir the extra virgin olive oil into the water then gradually add to the flour mixture. Stir well to combine. The dough should be smooth and slightly sticky. If the dough is too soupy, more flour can be added until a sticky dough forms.

3. Preheat the oven to 400°F. Lightly oil a 12 inch pizza sheet and add the dough.

4. Spread on a pizza pan and prepare your pizza!

5. Top with your favorite sauce, Vegan Mozzarella Cheese Balls, and your favorite toppings.

6. Bake pizza for about 15 minutes or until the crust is golden brown and the cheese is melted. Time will vary depending on if it's a thin or thick crust.

FETTUCCINE
alfredo

SERVINGS: 2 PEOPLE

PREP TIME: 5 MINS

COOK TIME: 20 MINS

TOTAL TIME: 25-30 MINS

INGREDIENTI

10 oz gluten-free pasta (linguini, spaghetti, or fusilli)
I bought 2 of the fresh fettuccine at Whole Foods.

4 garlic cloves, minced
2 tbsp extra virgin olive oil or ghee
1 cup unsalted cashews, soaked
1 3/4 cups vegetable broth
1/8 tsp onion powder *optional
1/8 - 1/4 tsp ground black pepper
¾ tsp tsp salt
¼ cup Vegan Parmesan Cheese (p 101)
Finely chopped parsley, to serve

NOTES
I like to blend garlic with sauce but you don't have to.

PREPARAZIONE

1. Make the pasta: Bring a large pot of salted water to a boil. Boil the pasta until it is al dente then drain the pasta and return it to the pot.

2. Meanwhile, prepare the sauce. Heat the extra virgin olive oil/ghee/vegan butter, in a large saucepan over medium heat.

3. Add the garlic and cook for 1-2 minutes until fragrant.

4. Meanwhile, in a blender add 1 cup of pre-soaked cashews, vegetable broth, black pepper, kosher salt, and Vegan Parmesan Cheese. Blend on high until a smooth sauce forms. Add the garlic and extra virgin olive oil*. Blend.

5. Bring to a simmer and combine it with pasta. Stir for 1-2 minutes.

6. Top with finely chopped parsley and serve immediately.

SPAGHETTI ALLA
carbonara

SERVINGS: 4

PREP TIME: 10 MINS

COOK TIME: 20 MINS

TOTAL TIME: 30 MINS

INGREDIENTI

1 (12 oz) package gluten-free spaghetti

4 egg yolks

4 oz pancetta

1 tsp turmeric powder

1 tsp paprika

3 tbsp nutritional yeast

Extra virgin olive oil

Salt and pepper to taste

PREPARAZIONE

1. Bring a large pot of salted water to a boil. Add the pasta and cook until al dente.

2. Meanwhile, heat a large skillet over medium heat, add the pancetta, and sauté until the fat just renders, on the edge of crispness but not hard. Remove from heat and set aside.

3. In a mixing bowl, whisk together the egg yolks, turmeric, paprika, and nutritional yeast. Season with a pinch of salt and generous black pepper.

4. Drain pasta and add to the skillet over low heat. Stir in the pancetta, and egg mixture for 1 minute or so, adding some water or a plant based milk if the mixture becomes too dry. Serve immediately.

RISOTTO

SERVINGS: 4

PREP TIME: 10 MINS

COOK TIME: 20 MINS

TOTAL TIME: 30 MINS

INGREDIENTI

1 ¼ cup Arborio rice

3-4 cups vegetable broth

2 tbsp extra virgin olive oil

1 yellow onion, chopped

¼ cup dry white wine *optional

¼ tsp black pepper

1 tsp salt

¼ cup Vegan Parmesan Cheese (p 101)

3 tbsp plant-based butter or ghee

Parsley

For Mushroom Risotto: 8 oz package of white mushrooms, rinsed and sliced.

For Asparagus Risotto: ½ lb asparagus, trim a ½ inch off the bottoms, and cut the spears into thin disks.

For Pumpkin Risotto: 2 cups cubed pumpkin. Use rosemary instead of parsley.

PREPARAZIONE

1. Heat 2 tbsp of extra virgin olive oil on medium heat.

2. Add onion and sauté until onion turns golden.

3. Add veggie of your choice and simmer for 3-4 minutes.

4. Add the white wine (if using) and reduce heat, simmer for 2 minutes. Turn off the heat.

5. Add Arborio rice and cook, stirring often for 2 minutes.

6. Pour half of the vegetable broth into the pot and bring to a boil. Stirring often, until broth is absorbed.

7. Repeat the process, adding small amounts of broth each time to the rice until all the broth has been absorbed.

8. The cooking process takes about 20 minutes to complete.

9. Taste the rice. It should be tender to the bite. Season with salt and pepper to taste.

10. When rice is fully cooked, turn OFF the heat. Add the final tablespoons of plant-based butter or ghee and Vegan Parmesan Cheese. Mix well to make a creamy risotto. Top it with Italian herbs (parsley or rosemary depending on the veggie you are using) and serve!

HOMEMADE MAC
and cheese

SERVINGS: 2

PREP TIME: 10 MINS

COOK TIME: 15 MINS

TOTAL TIME: 25 MINS

INGREDIENTI

8 oz gluten-free straight or elbow macaroni pasta

1 carrot, peeled

1 potato, peeled

⅓ cup unsalted raw cashews, soaked

⅓ cup nutritional yeast

1 cup vegetable broth

½ tsp sea salt

Pinch black pepper

PREPARAZIONE

1. Soak cashews in hot water for at least 15 minutes until soft.

2. Cut the potato and carrot into 1 inch cubes and cook in salted water for about 10-15 minutes until tender. Discard water afterward and set aside.

3. Boil gluten-free pasta as per instructions on the packaging.

4. Add cooked potato, carrot, drained cashews, salt, black pepper, nutritional yeast, and 1 cup vegetable broth in a high-speed blender.

5. Pour the sauce into a saucepan and bring it to a boil. Simmer for 1-2 minutes, stirring constantly.

6. Pour over pasta and serve immediately.

BROCCOLI SHRIMP
curry

SERVINGS: 2

PREP TIME: 15 MINS

COOK TIME: 10 MINS

TOTAL TIME: 25 MINS

INGREDIENTI

4 3/4 cups (12 oz) broccoli florets

2 tbsp coconut oil

3 garlic cloves, minced

1 tsp ginger powder

2 tbsp curry powder

2 (14 oz) cans coconut milk

1 tsp salt

¼ tsp cayenne pepper

1 (10 oz) bag of frozen peeled and deveined shrimp, thawed

PREPARAZIONE

1. First, wash the broccoli, cut it into florets, and set it aside.

2. Heat the oil in a nonstick pot or saucepan over medium-high temperature. Add minced garlic, ginger, curry, salt, and cayenne pepper. Stir continuously for about 1 minute.

3. Stir in broccoli and shrimp and mix it with spices. Add coconut milk and bring it to a simmer.

4. Cover the saucepan and cook for about 8 minutes until the broccoli florets are tender and shrimp is cooked. It will take at least 8 minutes to cook perfectly.

5. Serve immediately over rice or quinoa.

BUDDHA BOWL

SERVINGS: 2

PREP TIME: 10 MINS

COOK TIME: 30 MINS

TOTAL TIME: 40-45 MINS

INGREDIENTI

Precook 1 cup of basmati rice

For the Sweet Potato

1 medium sweet potato, cubed

¼ tsp turmeric

¼ tsp cumin

¼ tsp cinnamon

½ tsp Celtic salt

¼ tsp black pepper

1 tbsp coconut oil

Rosemary

For the Zucchini

2 small zucchini, diced or spiralized

½ tsp salt

¼ tsp pepper

¾ tsp ginger powder

2 tbsp extra virgin olive oil

For the Kale

A handful of kale

1-2 tbsp of water

Salt

½ lemon, juiced

For the Fried Chickpeas

1 can of chickpeas

2 tbsp extra virgin olive oil

¼ tsp cumin powder

¼ tsp turmeric powder

¼ tsp coriander powder

¼ tsp of paprika

½ tsp salt

1 tsp mixed Italian herbs

PREPARAZIONE

1. **Make the sweet potato.** Heat up the extra virgin olive oil in a pan and add the spices, then add the cubed sweet potato. Fry on low-medium heat for about 15-20 minutes until cooked.

2. **Make the zucchini.** Heat up the oil in a pan and add the spices, then add zucchini. Fry on low-medium heat for about 15-20 minutes until cooked.

3. **Make the fried chickpeas.** Heat up the oil in a pan and add the spices, then add drained chickpeas. Fry on low-medium heat for about 10 minutes until cooked.

4. **Make the kale.** Heat up water. Add kale, squeezed lemon juice, and salt. Fry on low-medium heat for about 5-10 minutes until steamed.

5. **Assemble.** Combine: rice, sweet potato, kale, zucchini, and chickpeas to make your bowl.

RAINBOW BOWL

SERVINGS: 1 BIG BOWL

PREP TIME: 15 MINS

COOK TIME: 10 MINS

TOTAL TIME: 25 MINS

INGREDIENTI

14 oz firm or extra firm tofu

2 tbsp extra virgin olive oil

2 tbsp toasted sesame oil

2 tbsp coconut aminos

½ lemon, juiced

1 cup basmati rice, cooked

1 cup purple cabbage, shredded

½ avocado, sliced

1 large carrot, peeled or grated

1 radish, sliced

½ medium cucumber

½ cup yellow corn

Sesame Ginger Miso dressing (p 87)

sesame seeds for garnish

PREPARAZIONE

1. Cut the tofu into large cubes (about 1 1/2x2 inches) and pat it dry with a towel. Add the extra virgin olive oil, sesame oil, coconut aminos, and lemon juice to a non-stick pan and add the tofu cubes.

2. Turn on the heat to medium-high. Cook for 5-6 minutes, flipping the tofu halfway through until lightly browned on the bottom. Garnish with sesame seeds.

3. Layer the rice, purple cabbage, carrots, corn, cucumber, radishes, ½ cup of cooked tofu, and avocado in small sections in the bowl.

4. Sprinkle with more sesame seeds.

5. Serve right away with sesame ginger miso dressing.

CHICKPEA TIKKA
masala

SERVINGS: 2

PREP TIME: 5 MINS

SOAKING TIME: 1 HOUR

COOK TIME: 20 MINS

TOTAL TIME:
1 HOUR 25 MINS

INGREDIENTI

For The Marinated Chickpeas

1 can chickpeas, organic

½ cup plant-based plain yogurt

½ tsp each of garam masala, paprika, salt, and turmeric

2 tsp ginger paste or minced ginger

2 tsp garlic paste or minced, or 3/4 tsp garlic powder

2 tsp lemon juice

1 tsp nutritional yeast *optional

1 tbsp extra virgin olive oil

For The Sauce (Tikka Masala)

1 tbsp extra virgin olive oil or plant-based butter

3 garlic cloves, finely chopped

1 (15 oz) can diced tomatoes or 3 large ripe tomatoes

1 inch cube of ginger, chopped in half

½ hot or mild green chile julienned or thinly sliced, or use very thinly sliced green bell pepper

½ cup canned coconut cream or vegan yogurt

½ tsp garam masala

½ tsp paprika

⅛ tsp or less of cayenne pepper

½ cup water

¼ tsp cumin powder

½ tsp salt

½ tsp sugar or another sweetener to preference *optional

cilantro to garnish

PREPARAZIONE

1. In a bowl, mix the chickpeas and the rest of the ingredients together with plant-based yogurt. Cover and keep the marinated chickpeas in the refrigerator for 1 hour.

2. Bake chickpeas at 350˚F for about 30 minutes, turning once or twice.

3. In a blender, puree the diced tomato with the chopped ginger and half the green chile, water, and vegan yogurt/cream. Set aside.

4. Heat oil/plant-based butter in a skillet over medium heat. Add garlic and cook until golden. Then add spices, salt, and sugar and mix well.

5. Add the puree to the skillet and cook until it starts to thicken and does not taste raw tomatoey. Mix and bring to a boil. Taste and adjust salt, heat (add cayenne) and sweetener. Add more water if needed for preferred consistency. Fold in the baked chickpeas. Simmer for 1 minute. Garnish with cilantro. Serve over rice.

KITCHARI

SERVINGS: 2

PREP TIME: 10 MINS

COOK TIME: 1 HOUR

TOTAL TIME:
1 HOUR 10 MINS

INGREDIENTI

1 cup white arborio rice

½ cup red lentils

2 tbsp ghee

¼ tsp black mustard seeds

½ tsp cumin seeds

½ tsp turmeric powder

1 ½ tsp coriander powder

½ tsp fennel powder

1 tsp fresh ginger, grated

1 tsp natural mineral salt

4-6 cups water

1 cup easily digestible vegetables (such as asparagus, carrots, celery, green beans, summer squash, sweet potato, winter squash, or zucchini)

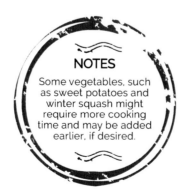

NOTES
Some vegetables, such as sweet potatoes and winter squash might require more cooking time and may be added earlier, if desired.

PREPARAZIONE

1. Rinse rice and lentils, and set aside.

2. In a medium saucepan or soup pot, warm the ghee over medium heat. Add the black mustard seeds and cumin seeds. Sauté for a couple of minutes, until the mustard seeds begin to pop. Add turmeric, coriander, fennel, and fresh ginger. Stir briefly.

3. Stir the rice and red lentils mixture into the spices and sauté for a few moments, stirring constantly.

4. Add the 4 cups of water, turn the heat to high, and bring to a boil. When it comes to a boil, stir in the salt, reduce heat, cover, and simmer for about 40 minutes.

5. Meanwhile, cut your vegetables into small, bite-sized pieces. About halfway through the cooking process, stir in the vegetables and allow the stew to return to a boil. Continue to simmer until the rice, lentil, and vegetables are fully cooked. Add extra 2 cups of water if needed. Remove from heat, cool, and serve.

KALE BUCKWHEAT
salad

SERVINGS: 2

PREP TIME: 15 MINS

COOK TIME: 5 - 10 MINS

TOTAL TIME: 25 MINS

INGREDIENTI

1 cup buckwheat

½ cup walnuts, toasted

½ cup raisins

½ large lemon or 1 small lemon, juiced

½ a long English cucumber, diced into ¼ inch pieces

1 small bunch (about 3 cups) of Tuscan kale, stemmed and finely shredded

1 small red onion, sliced

Italian Dressing (p 87)

PREPARAZIONE

1. Cook the buckwheat as per instructions on the packaging.

2. Meanwhile, juice lemon on the finely shredded Tuscan kale and massage it gently.

3. Toast the walnut on a non-stick pan for 1-3 minutes.

4. Rinse cooked buckwheat with cold water using a strainer.

5. Combine buckwheat, walnut, raisins, cucumber, Tuscan kale, and red onion in a large bowl. Season the kale buckwheat salad with Italian Dressing and serve.

AYURVEDIC QUINOA
salad

SERVINGS: 4

PREP TIME: 20 MINS

COOK TIME: 10-15 MINS

TOTAL TIME: 30-35 MINS

INGREDIENTI

1 cup organic quinoa, rinsed

2 tbsp extra virgin olive oil

1 lime, juiced

2 tbsp coconut aminos

2 scallion stalks, diced

½ cup corn

½ cup kale, finely chopped

½ red bell pepper, diced

½ orange bell pepper, diced

1 cucumber, chopped into small cubes

⅓ cup cilantro, chopped

To make the Chickpeas:

1 can of chickpeas

2 tbsp extra virgin olive oil

½ tsp cumin powder

½ tsp turmeric powder

½ tsp coriander powder

½ tsp of paprika

½ tsp salt

1 tsp mixed Italian herbs

PREPARAZIONE

1. Combine the rinsed quinoa and water in a medium saucepan over medium-high heat. Bring to a boil then reduce to a low simmer and cook, uncovered, until the liquid is absorbed by the quinoa, about 10-15 minutes. Move the saucepan off of the heat and cover for 5 minutes. This extra time allows the quinoa to steam and "fluff up." Uncover, and then fluff the quinoa with a fork. Set aside to cool slightly.

2. **To make the chickpeas.** In a separate pan, heat 2 tbsp of extra virgin olive oil and add cumin, turmeric, coriander, paprika, salt, and mixed Italian herbs. Add your cooked chickpeas to the pot and sauté until the spices, herbs, and chickpeas "marry." Put your cooked chickpeas in a bowl and set them aside.

3. **Make the salad.** When the quinoa has cooled slightly, in a large bowl combine the quinoa, chickpeas, cucumber, bell pepper, kale, cilantro, corn, and scallion with coconut aminos, lime juice, and extra virgin olive oil. Mix well and serve.

BURGER

SERVINGS: 4

PREP TIME: 15 MINS

COOK TIME: 10 MINS

TOTAL TIME: 25 MINS

INGREDIENTI

4 gluten-free buns

1 lb organic ground beef

½ tsp garlic powder

1 tsp smoked paprika

¼ tsp black pepper

1 tsp salt

Sliced tomatoes

Sliced pickles

Buttercrunch lettuce leaves

1 red onion, sliced

Sliced avocado

Veganaise

Yellow mustard

PREPARAZIONE

1. Make the burger patties by adding the ground beef, salt, garlic powder, paprika, and black pepper to a large bowl. Mix with clean hands until evenly combined. Divide into four, 4 oz, portions and shape into ¼-½ inch patties.

2. To grill, place each burger onto a preheated grill or grill pan. Cook for 3 minutes on one side and then flip and cook for another 3 minutes or until burgers register 160˚F. At the same time as the burgers cook, grill the red onion slices, if desired.

3. Serve on toasted gluten-free buns with buttercrunch lettuce, tomatoes, grilled onion, avocado, pickles, veganaise, yellow mustard, or other condiments. Enjoy!

BLACK BEAN
tacos

SERVINGS: 4

PREP TIME: 15 MINS

COOK TIME: 20 MINS

TOTAL TIME: 35 MINS

FOR THE BLACK BEANS

½ onion, chopped

1 tbsp extra virgin olive oil

1 tsp crushed garlic

¼ tsp cayenne pepper

¼ tsp chili flakes

½ tsp ground cumin

1 (15 oz) can black beans, drained

Salt and pepper to taste

PICO DE GALLO

4 large tomatoes, chopped

½ cup cilantro, chopped

½ medium onion, chopped

½ tsp crushed garlic

1 tbsp lime juice, freshly squeezed

1 tbsp extra virgin olive oil

Sea salt and black pepper, to taste

TAHINI SAUCE

½ cup tahini

¼ cup lemon juice

2 tsp maple syrup

½ tsp salt

½ tsp garlic powder

¼ cup water

FOR THE TOFU

14 oz extra firm tofu, drained

2 tbsp extra virgin olive oil

2 tbsp sesame seed oil

2 tbsp coconut aminos

2 tbsp sesame seeds

Juice of ½ lemon

FOR ASSEMBLING

2–3 cups lettuce, shredded

2 avocados, peeled and chopped

12–16 corn tortillas

PREPARAZIONE

1. Make the beans. Add the chopped onion to a pan along with the extra virgin olive oil, crushed garlic, cayenne pepper, chili flakes and ground cumin and sauté until the onions are softened. Add in the black beans and sauté with the onions and spices until heated through. If it's getting too dry in the pan then add in a little water. Add salt and pepper to taste.

2. Pico de gallo. Add the chopped tomatoes, cilantro and onion to a mixing bowl. Add in the crushed garlic, fresh lime juice and extra virgin olive oil and toss everything together until well mixed. Add sea salt and black pepper to taste.

3. Prepare the tofu. Cut the tofu into large cubes (about 1 ½ x 2 inch) and pat it dry with a towel. Add the extra virgin olive oil, sesame oil, coconut aminos, and lemon juice to a non-stick pan and add the tofu cubes. Turn on the heat to medium-high. Cook for 5-6 minutes flipping the tofu halfway through until lightly browned on the bottom. Garnish with sesame seeds.

4. Prepare your shredded lettuce and chopped avocado.

5. Heat your tortillas using your preferred method, or by lightly frying in a pan, or stacking them up and covering in foil and baking in the oven at 350°F for around 15 minutes, until heated through.

6. Assemble your tacos. by adding some shredded lettuce to a tortilla, followed by some black beans, tofu, then pico de gallo, then chopped avocado, and top with a drizzle of tahini sauce.

COLLARD GREEN-RAINBOW
wrap

SERVINGS: 1 WRAP

PREP TIME: 15 MINS

TOTAL TIME: 15 MINS

INGREDIENTI

1 collard green leaf

2 tbsp hummus

2 oz firm tofu, sliced

¾ cup fresh beets, julienned

¾ cup red cabbage, thinly shredded

¾ cup carrots, julienned

¼ cup sprouts

PREPARAZIONE

1. Cut the stem off of the collard green leaf and then shave it down using a small knife so that it is flat. This will help prevent the collard leaf from breaking at the end and make it easier to roll up.

2. Spread leaf with hummus. Top with beets, sprouts, cabbage, tofu, and carrots to the middle-bottom of each collard leaf.

3. Roll the collard wrap up just like you would a burrito, tucking in the ends as you go so that the filling stays inside.

4. Slice the wraps in half.

NOTES
Serve wraps with a side of brown rice, and if you desire, a Dressing (p 86) of your choice for dipping.

BABY SCALLOPS WITH
garlic

SERVINGS: 4

PREP TIME: 10 MINS

COOK TIME: 10 MINS

TOTAL TIME: 20 MINS

INGREDIENTI

1 lb baby scallops, frozen

⅓ cup gluten-free flour mix

3-4 tbsp of extra virgin olive oil or plant-based butter

2 garlic clove, minced

Salt to taste

Black pepper to taste

Parsley, chopped for garnish

Lemon wedges, for serving

PREPARAZIONE

1. Leave baby scallops out to defrost. Put the flour in a shallow bowl, roll the scallops in the flour to lightly coat, dusting off any excess.

2. Heat the extra virgin olive oil over medium-high heat. Add garlic and sauté for 30 seconds.

3. Add scallops and cook for 2-5 minutes, scooping and turning often, until color turns from translucent to opaque (white). Do not overcook.

4. Garnish the scallops with chopped parsley and serve with lemon wedges, if desired.

5. Serve with hot cooked pasta, or rice, along with sautéed spinach or swiss chard.

LEMON SAGE
chicken bites

SERVINGS: 4

PREP TIME: 5 MINS

COOK TIME: 15 MINS

TOTAL TIME: 20 MINS

INGREDIENTI

4 (16 oz) boneless skinless chicken breasts

½ tsp salt

¼ tsp fresh ground pepper to taste

2 tbsp ghee or vegan butter (Earth Balance)

2 garlic cloves, minced

10 fresh Italian sage leaves

1 lemon, juiced

PREPARAZIONE

1. Cut chicken into 1 inch cubes.

2. Add the ghee or vegan butter to a large skillet and heat over medium heat.

3. Add salt, pepper, garlic, and sage. Stir for 1 minutes. Make sure the sage doesn't burn.

4. Add the chicken breast and cook for 6-8 minutes until golden on one side, then add lemon juice and cook for another 2 minutes.

5. Serve with a side dish.

SALMON WITH
blueberry sauce

SERVINGS: 4

PREP TIME: 10 MINS

COOK TIME: 10 MINS

TOTAL TIME: 20 MINS

INGREDIENTI

1 lb boneless, skinless, uncooked farmed Atlantic salmon cut into 4 filets

Cooking spray

Blueberry Sauce

1 cup fresh blueberries

5-6 sprigs of fresh thyme

1 tbsp granulated sugar

1 tbsp balsamic vinegar

2 tsp lemon juice

½ tsp salt

PREPARAZIONE

1. **Blueberry sauce.** In a small sauce pot, add the blueberries, thyme, sugar, balsamic vinegar, lemon juice, and ¼ tsp of salt. Place over medium heat. Boil for 15 minutes, stirring occasionally. The blueberries will release their juices. The sauce will reduce and thicken. Turn off and set aside.

2. **Salmon.** Coat a grill or grill pan with cooking spray, heat to medium-high heat. Grill salmon until cooked to the desired degree of doneness, flipping once, for 4-5 minutes per side.

Serve salmon with Blueberry Sauce spooned over top.

Salmon is also great with this Spicy Mango Salsa as a variation.

1 large ripe, diced peach

¾ cup ripe, diced mango

¼ cup raw red onion, minced

2 tbsp fresh cilantro, minced

1 small jalapeño pepper, seeded and minced

2 tsp fresh lime juice

½ tsp honey

½ tsp extra virgin olive oil

SWORDFISH
alla siciliana

SERVINGS: 2

PREP TIME: 5 MINS

COOK TIME: 15 MINS

TOTAL TIME: 20 MINS

INGREDIENTI

2 swordfish steaks

1 garlic clove, minced

2 tbsp extra virgin olive oil

1 pint container of fresh cherry tomatoes, chopped

⅓ cup green olives, pitted and minced

2 oz of pine nuts

Black pepper & salt, to taste

Pinch of oregano

PREPARAZIONE

1. **Siciliana sauce.** Rinse and dry cherry tomatoes, then cut them in half.

2. In a large pan heat the oil over high heat and add garlic. Sauté for a couple of minutes, then add cherry tomatoes and reduce heat to low-medium heat for about 8-10 minutes.

3. Add olives, black pepper, salt, pine nuts and oregano.

4. **Swordfish.** Add swordfish steaks and cook for a few minutes on each side.

5. Serve the swordfish with the Siciliana sauce.

PORK CHOPS WITH
maple pear sauce

SERVINGS: 4

PREP TIME: 10 MINS

COOK TIME: 10 MINS

TOTAL TIME: 20 MINS

INGREDIENTI

4 boneless pork chops cut ¾ inch thick (about 1 lb)

½ tsp kosher salt or sea salt

½ tsp ground black pepper

1 tbsp extra virgin olive oil

¼ cup plant-based butter

3 tbsp pure maple syrup or maple-flavored syrup

3 tbsp peach, apricot or plum preserves, or jam

½ tsp dried basil or 1 ½ tsp snipped fresh basil

3 medium pears, cored and thinly sliced

PREPARAZIONE

1. Trim fat from pork. Sprinkle chops with salt and pepper. In a 10 inch skillet, heat oil over medium-high heat.

2. Cook chops for 8-12 minutes or till chops reach a temperature of 160°F and juices run clear, turning once. Remove chops from skillet; cover to keep warm and set aside.

3. In the same skillet, melt butter over medium heat. Stir in maple syrup, desired fruit preserves, and basil. Add pears. Cook for about 3 minutes or just until the pears are tender and heated through, occasionally spooning sauce over the pears.

4. Serve each chop with a spoonful of sauce over pork and your favorite side dish.

SOUFFLÉ

You will need

2 Ramekin pans or a 6x2 inch aluminum round cake pans

Stand up-mixer or hand mixer

SERVINGS: 4

PREP TIME: 10 MINS

COOK TIME: 25 MINS

TOTAL TIME: 35 MINS

INGREDIENTI

3 tbsp plant-based butter, plus more for greasing the dish

Gluten-free flour mix for dusting the dish

2 ½ tsp tapioca starch

1 cup alternative milk

4 large egg yolks

5 large cold egg whites

3 oz freshly grated plant-based Parmigiano

½ tsp cream of tartar

¼ tsp nutmeg

Salt and freshly ground black pepper to taste

PREPARAZIONE

1. Preheat the oven to 375°F. Set the oven rack in lowest position. Grease the interior of 2 Ramekin pans or a 6x2 inch aluminum round cake pan. Add some gluten-free flour, rotating the ramekin all around so flour sticks to every part of the buttered surface. Set aside.

2. **To make the white sauce.** In a small saucepan, melt 3 tablespoons of plant-based butter over medium-high heat (do not allow it to brown). Add tapioca starch and whisk to form a paste. Whisking constantly, add milk in a thin, steady stream, or in increments of a couple of tablespoons at a time, whisking thoroughly and getting into all corners of the pan to maintain a lump-free texture. The sauce will initially become very thick, then get thin once all the milk is added. Add salt, pepper, and nutmeg. Reduce heat to low and cook, stirring and scraping the sides and bottom of the pan, until sauce is nicely thickened in about 3 minutes. Set aside and allow to cool slightly.

3. Meanwhile, in a large mixing bowl, using a stand mixer or an electric hand whisk, combine egg whites with cream of tartar and beat until firm glossy peaks form.

4. Add ⅓ of the beaten egg whites to the white sauce base and stir well until the whites are thoroughly combined and the soufflé base has a looser consistency. Mix in the plant-based Parmigiano cheese and then add the remaining beaten whites. Using a silicone spatula, gently fold the egg whites into the soufflé base just until well combined.

5. Scrape soufflé batter into the prepared baking dish, filling it up to the inner ridge, not to the top. If desired, using an offset or other spatula, gently smooth and level the surface of the soufflé batter.

6. Bake until puffed and lightly browned, 20-25 minutes or until done. Serve immediately.

PORK RIBS WITH
cherry bbq sauce

SERVINGS: 4

PREP TIME: 10 MINS

COOK TIME:
2 HRS 10 MINS

TOTAL TIME:
2 HRS 20 MINS

INGREDIENTI

2-2 ½ lbs baby back pork ribs

Salt and black pepper

Rosemary

Cherry BBQ Sauce

½ cup frozen, pitted cherries

½ onion, finely chopped

4 carrots, chopped

¼ cup bone broth

2 tbsp molasses

2 tbsp maple syrup

1 tbsp fresh lemon juice

1 tbsp apple cider vinegar

¼ tsp black pepper

½ tsp salt

PREPARAZIONE

1. Heat oven to 320°F. If the ribs still have the thin membrane covering the back of the rack, remove it.

2. Season both sides of the ribs with a generous amount of salt, pepper and rosemary. Place the ribs, meat-side up, into a large roasting pan or rimmed baking sheet (it may be necessary to cut the ribs in half for them to fit into the pan).

3. Cover the pan or baking sheet tightly with aluminum foil, and bake for 2 hours.

4. Heat oven to 400°F. Take off the aluminum foil and bake for 10 minutes. Add more time if necessary. You will know ribs are done when the meat is cooked through and tender. This depends on the size of the ribs. Serve with cherry BBQ sauce.

5. **Cherry BBQ Sauce.** In a saucepan, add the carrots to 1 cup of water. Bring to a boil, lower the heat to a simmer and cook for about 6 minutes or until carrots are fork tender. Drain carrots. In the saucepan over medium-high heat, add cherries, onion, and broth. Bring to a boil, then lower the heat to a simmer. Add the remaining ingredients and cook on medium-low heat for 20-25 minutes, stirring occasionally. Transfer the mixture to a food processor or high-speed blender. Blend until combined, and store in the refrigerator while making ribs.

FRITTATA
di patate

SERVINGS: 4

PREP TIME: 5 MINS

COOK TIME: 15 MINS

TOTAL TIME: 20 MINS

INGREDIENTI

1 lb potatoes, peeled and cubed

6 large eggs

3 tbsp milk alternative

½ salt

¼ tsp pepper

2 small green onions, finely chopped

1 tbsp plant-based butter

1 tbsp nutritional yeast

PREPARAZIONE

1. Bring a pot full of water to a boil and cook cubed potatoes for 4-5 minutes. Drain and set aside.

2. Meanwhile, in a medium bowl, whisk together the eggs, green onion, milk alternative, salt, and pepper until well combined. Stir in the nutritional yeast.

3. Heat up the plant-based butter in a non-stick pan over low-medium heat. Pour over drained potatoes.

4. Carefully pour over the egg mixture, smoothing the top. Turn to low heat and cover with a lid.

5. Cook for 15-20 minutes, just until the eggs are set (the cooking time may vary based on your skillet, so keep an eye on it). Slice and serve immediately.

PINEAPPLE CAULIFLOWER
fried rice

SERVINGS: 2

PREP TIME: 10 MINS

COOK TIME: 20 MINS

TOTAL TIME: 30 MINS

INGREDIENTI

3 tbsp extra virgin olive oil, divided

2 eggs, beaten with a dash of salt

1 ½ cups fresh pineapple, chopped

1 large red bell pepper, diced

¾ cup green onions, chopped

2 garlic cloves, pressed or minced

½ cup raw, unsalted cashews, chopped

12 oz frozen cauliflower rice

1 tbsp coconut aminos

½ tsp ginger powder

¼ cayenne pepper

1 small lime, juiced

Salt, to taste

A handful of fresh cilantro leaves, torn into little pieces, for garnishing

PREPARAZIONE

1. Heat 1 tbsp oil in a large non-stick frying pan over medium-high heat. Pour in the eggs and cook, stirring frequently, until the eggs are scrambled and lightly set, about 30 seconds to 1 minute. Transfer the eggs to an empty bowl.

2. Heat 1 tbsp extra virgin olive oil in the pan, then add the pineapple and red pepper. Cook, stirring constantly until the liquid has evaporated and the pineapple is caramelized on the edges, about 3-5 minutes. Then add the green onion, garlic, and ginger. Cook until fragrant while stirring constantly, about 30 seconds. Transfer the contents of the pan to your bowl of eggs.

3. Reduce the heat to medium and add the remaining 1 tbsp oil to the pan. Pour in the cashews and cook until fragrant, stirring constantly for about 30 seconds. Add the frozen cauliflower rice to the pan and stir to combine. Cook until the frozen cauliflower rice is hot, stirring occasionally, about 2-3 minutes.

4. Pour the contents of the bowl back into the pan and stir to combine, breaking up the scrambled eggs with a spoon. Cook until the contents are warmed through, then remove the pan from heat. Add coconut aminos. Squeeze the juice of 1 lime over the dish and stir to combine. Season to taste with salt and sprinkle with cilantro.

NOTES

Substitute cauliflower rice with 2 cups cooked basmati rice, if desired.

Avocado Chocolate Mousse (p 217)

Desserts

SALAME AL CIOCCOLATO

SERVINGS: 10

PREP TIME: 15 MINS

REST TIME: 4 HOURS

TOTAL TIME:
4 HRS 15 MINS

INGREDIENTI

1 ⅓ cup of dark chocolate chips, dairy-free

1 package of graham crackers, gluten-free and dairy-free

1 ½ stick (6 oz) of Earth Balance butter

1 egg, room temperature

½ cup white cane sugar

Powdered sugar for topping

PREPARAZIONE

1. Coarsely crumble the dry graham crackers. Use your hands and not the blender, as you don't wanro over mix. You should feel the pieces inside the salame.

2. Melt the dark chocolate in a double boiler. While the chocolate is melting, whip the plant-based butter with sugar and then the egg. Mix well until you get a smooth and homogeneous cream.

3. Add the warmed melted chocolate to the mixture of butter, sugar and egg. Knead the chocolate salame mixture until it becomes perfectly homogeneous, then add the chopped graham crackers and mix.

4. Place the mixture on a sheet of baking paper and try to give it a salami shape as regular as possible, using your hands and a spatula. Once you have given it the shape, roll it in the paper until it forms a large cylindrical candy. Squeeze the sides well and then roll it up in the same way in aluminum foil.

5. Put it to rest in the refrigerator for at least 4 hours.

6. Once it has hardened, take it out of the fridge, remove the aluminum and baking paper and roll it in powdered sugar. Serve the chocolate salame in slices, just like a real salami.

PANNA COTTA

SERVINGS: 6

PREP TIME: 5 MINS

REST TIME: 1 HOUR

COOK TIME: 10 MINS

TOTAL TIME: 1 HR 15 MINS

INGREDIENTI

2 (14 oz) cans coconut milk or other milk of your choice

3-5 tbsp maple syrup (or more)

1 tbsp powdered agar agar

1 tsp vanilla extract

Raspberry Topping

2 cups raspberries, fresh or frozen (or any type of berries)

4 tbsp white sugar

1 tbsp fresh lemon juice

½ cup water

PREPARAZIONE

1. Add coconut milk, vanilla extract, and sugar to a medium saucepan and set over medium/high heat. Bring to a boil (or at least 185°F), then whisk in agar agar. Continue boiling for 3 minutes, watching to ensure it doesn't spill over.

2. Pour mixture into 6 individual serving bowls or ramekins (3 ½ inches in diameter).

3. Place in the fridge to cool until set, about 1 hour.

4. Meanwhile, add raspberries, sugar, lemon, and water to a medium saucepan. Cook uncovered over medium heat for 10-15 minutes, until raspberries have broken down and the mixture has thickened.

5. Flip each ramekin onto a serving plate and top with desired fruit topping.

TIRAMISÚ

for Gluten-free Lady Fingers
(Makes about 24)

INGREDIENTI

⅓ cup gluten free flour mix

1 tsp baking powder, gluten-free and aluminum-free

4 large eggs whites, at room temperature

3 large egg yolks

⅓ cup white sugar

1 tsp pure vanilla extract

½ tsp salt

Powdered sugar for topping

COOK TIME: 25 MINS

PREP TIME: 10 MINS

TOTAL TIME: 35 MINS

SERVINGS: 4

PREPARAZIONE

1. Preheat the oven to 350˚F.

2. With a hand mixer, beat egg whites with 1 tbsp of the ⅓ cup of white sugar, reserving the rest, until stiff peaks form.

3. Gently scrape the beaten egg whites out of the mixing bowl into another medium-sized bowl. Set the egg whites aside.

4. In the original mixing bowl, place the egg yolks and the remaining sugar. Turn the mixer on medium-high speed and beat until the sugar is absorbed into the yolks, about 1 minute.

5. Add vanilla extract, baking powder, and salt. Turn the mixer speed up to high and continue to beat for 8-10 minutes on medium speed, or until the mixture is pale yellow, thick, and nearly tripled in volume. Don't skimp on this step!

6. Remove the bowl from your stand mixer and add about ¼ of the whipped egg whites. Folding in this small amount first will loosen up the batter. Add the remaining egg whites, carefully folding them in.

7. Using a sifter, sift ⅓ of the flour at a time over the egg white mixture, and with a flexible rubber spatula or whisk, start folding the flour into the wet ingredients. Make sure to combine everything and there are no pockets of flour.

Piping and Baking Ladyfingers

1. Transfer the ladyfinger cookie batter to a piping bag fitted with a plain, round piping tip.

2. Pipe 3-4 inch "fingers" onto the prepared baking sheet making sure there are at last 2 inches between the cookies to provide room for them to rise and spread.

3. Using a small sifter, evenly dust the unbaked ladyfingers with powdered sugar.

4. Bake both sheet trays of ladyfingers at the same time at 350°F for 10-15 minutes. The ladyfingers should be golden brown and crunchy-looking.

5. Turn off the oven and allow the cookies to cool down. Set aside.

for Dairy-free Mascarpone Cream

INGREDIENTI

2 eggs

¼ cup of white sugar

Unsweetened cacao powder to sift on top

1 (8 oz) plant-based cream cheese container

1 tsp vanilla extract

PREP TIME: 25 MINS

COOK TIME: 15 MINS

TOTAL TIME: 40 MINS

PREPARAZIONE

1. Carefully separate the egg whites from the yolks, remembering that to whip the egg whites well they must not contain any trace of yolk.

2. Then whip the egg yolks with a hand mixer, pouring in only half of the sugar. As soon as the mixture has become clear and frothy, and with the mixer still running, add plant-based cream cheese and vanilla, little by little, until you obtain a thick and compact cream. Set it aside.

3. Clean the mixer attachments very well and beat the egg whites, pouring in the remaining sugar a little at a time. Whisk them into stiff peaks; you will know they are ready if the mixture does not move when you overturn the bowl.

4. Take a spoonful of egg whites and pour it into the bowl with egg yolks and sugar and stir vigorously with a spatula, to thin the mixture. Then proceed to add the remaining egg whites, little by little, stirring very gently from bottom to top.

You will need an 8x11 inch pan

MAKE THE TIRAMISÙ

INGREDIENTI

Gluten-free ladyfingers

Dairy-free mascarpone cream

8-12 oz black coffee

1. Soak the ladyfingers for a few moments in the cooled coffee, first on one side and then the other. Arrange the soaked ladyfingers, side by side, to create the first layer, over which you will spread part of the plant-based cheese cream (dairy-free mascarpone cheese).
2. Make sure to level it carefully so that you have a smooth surface. Using a sifter, sprinkle it with unsweetened cacao powder.
3. Continue to arrange the coffee-soaked ladyfingers, then add another layer of cream.
4. Repeat step 2 and then allow it to sit in the fridge for a couple of hours before serving.

Almond Flour Chocolate Chip Cookies (p 191)

Celtic Sea Salt Chocolate Brownie Cookies (p 194)

ALMOND FLOUR CHOCOLATE
chip cookies

SERVINGS: 9-12

PREP TIME: 15 MINS

COOK TIME: 13-15 MINS

TOTAL TIME: 30 MINS

INGREDIENTI

1 ¼ cup almond flour

¾ tsp baking powder

¼ tsp baking soda

½ tsp salt

4 tbsp unsalted plant-based butter, softened

⅓ cup almond butter

¾ cup + 2 tbsp coconut sugar

1 large egg

1 tsp vanilla extract

1 cup chocolate chips, dairy-free

PREPARAZIONE

1. Preheat the oven to 375°F, and line two large cookie sheet pans with parchment paper.

2. In a small bowl, whisk together the almond flour, baking powder, baking soda, and salt. Set aside.

3. In a medium bowl, add the softened butter and almond butter, and beat until creamy, about 3 minutes. Add the brown sugar and beat for another 2 minutes to combine.

4. Add the egg and vanilla to the butter mixture, and beat just to combine.

5. Add the dry ingredients to the bowl with the wet ingredients and stir to combine everything. Finally, stir in the chocolate chips.

6. Using a cookie scoop, portion out 9 big (or 12 small-medium) dough scoops onto the baking sheets.

7. Bake, rotating the pans halfway through for 13-15 minutes. The cookies are done when the edges start to turn golden brown. As they cool, they will deflate.

8. Let cookies cool for 1-2 minutes on the cookie sheet before moving them to the cool rack. Enjoy immediately, or keep covered at room temperature for up to 3 days.

SUGAR COOKIES

SERVINGS: 20-24 COOKIES

PREP TIME:

1 HR + 15 MINS

COOK TIME: 10-12 MINS
TOTAL TIME: 1 HR 27 MINS

INGREDIENTI

1 cup sugar

½ cup Earth Balance butter, softened

1 large egg

1 tbsp water or milk alternative

1 ½ tsp vanilla extract

¼ tsp salt

¼ tsp ground cinnamon *optional*

½ tsp xanthan gum (omit if your all-purpose flour has it)

2 cups gluten-free all-purpose flour, plus more for rolling/dusting

For the Icing

3 cups confectioners' sugar

½ tsp pure vanilla extract

4 ½ –5 tbsp room temperature water

pinch salt

PREPARAZIONE

1. In a large bowl, cream the sugar and plant-based butter at medium speed.

2. Add the egg, water or milk alternative, vanilla extract, salt, and cinnamon (if using). Blend until mixed well.

3. Add the xanthan gum (if using) and flour. Mix at a low speed until well combined.

4. Cover and refrigerate for at least 1 hour.

5. Preheat the oven to 350°F. Line a baking sheet with parchment paper and set it aside.

6. Roll out the dough onto a lightly floured surface, about ¼-inch thick.

7. Cut out the dough with selected cookie cutters, and place the cookies on the baking sheet. Make sure the cookies are not touching.

8. Reform and roll out the scrap dough, then continue cutting more cookies.

9. Bake for 10-12 minutes. Remove from the oven, and let the cookies cool for 5 minutes on the cookie sheet before moving them to a cooling rack. Cool completely before decorating.

10. **For the Icing.** Stir together the sugar, water, vanilla, and a pinch of salt in a medium-sized bowl until combined. If coloring the icing with different colors, divide it into bowls and color as desired at this point. Transfer icing to a piping bag with a piping tip. Pipe icing onto cookies and decorate, as desired.

11. Store in an airtight container for up to 5 days.

CELTIC SEA SALT CHOCOLATE
brownie cookies

SERVINGS: 11-12

PREP TIME: 10 MINS

REST TIME: 50 MINS

COOK TIME: 12-15 MINS

TOTAL TIME:
1 HR 15 MINS

INGREDIENTI

1 cup all-purpose gluten-free flour

⅔ cup unsweetened cocoa powder

1 tsp baking soda

⅛ pink Himalayan salt

½ cup + 2 tbsp plant-based unsalted butter

½ cup brown sugar

½ cup cane sugar

1 large egg

1 tsp vanilla extract

2 tbsp dairy-free milk (of your choice)

¾ cup of chocolate chips, dairy-free

Celtic sea salt (for topping)

PREPARAZIONE

1. Whisk the flour, cocoa powder, baking soda, and salt together until combined. Set aside.

2. In a large bowl, using a hand-held or stand mixer fitted with a paddle attachment, beat the butter for 1 minute on medium speed until completely smooth and creamy.

3. Add the granulated sugar and brown sugar and beat on medium-high speed until fluffy and light in color.

4. Beat in egg and vanilla on high speed. Scrape down the sides and bottom of the bowl as needed.

5. On low speed, slowly mix the dry ingredients into the wet ingredients until combined.

6. The cookie dough will be sticky. Cover dough tightly with aluminum foil or plastic wrap and chill for at least 30 minutes.

7. Remove cookie dough from the fridge and allow it to sit at room temperature for 20 minutes until ready to scoop. Preheat the oven to 375˚F. Line two large baking sheets with parchment paper.

8. Scoop and roll into balls of dough, about 2 tbsp of dough each, and press on each to flatten. Place on the baking sheets and sprinkle with Celtic sea salt.

9. Bake the cookies for 12-15 minutes. Allow cooling for 5 minutes on the cooking sheet. Transfer to the cooling rack to cool completely.

APPLE CRUMBLE

SERVINGS: 3-4

PREP TIME: 10 MINS

COOK TIME: 30 MINS

TOTAL TIME: 40 MINS

INGREDIENTI

4 medium Granny Smith apples, peeled, cored, and sliced or diced into bite-sized pieces

Pinch of salt

1 tsp pumpkin spice

1 tbsp monk fruit sugar

½ lemon, juiced

2 tbsp ghee/plant-based butter or coconut oil*

Crumble Topping

½ cup rolled oats, certified gluten-free

¼ cup almond flour

¼ cup brown sugar

½ tsp cinnamon

3 tbsp ghee/plant-based butter or coconut oil

*Notes**

Whatever oil/butter you choose to use in the apple mixture, make sure you use it for the crumble topping. For example, If you are using coconut oil, make sure you use it for both apple mixture and crumble topping so that the flavor is the same.

PREPARAZIONE

1. Preheat the oven to 375°F. Lightly spray a 9 inch loaf pan with nonstick cooking spray and set aside.

2. In a non-stick pan on low-medium heat combine apples, monk fruit sugar, lemon juice, plant-based butter/ghee or coconut oil (depending on what you are using), and pumpkin spice. Mix well and saute for 5-10 minutes until tender.

3. Transfer the apple mixture to the prepared baking dish and spread it into an even layer.

4. Meanwhile, in a medium bowl combine crumble topping ingredients. Whisk to combine.

5. Sprinkle the crumble mixture evenly over the top of the filling.

6. Bake for 20-30 minutes or until bubbling and golden brown on top.

7. Let cool for 15 minutes before serving with dairy-free ice cream, if desired.

BLUEBERRY MUFFINS

SERVINGS: 12

PREP TIME: 10 MINS

COOK TIME: 30-35 MINS

TOTAL TIME: 45 MINS

INGREDIENTI

½ cup avocado oil

¾ cup coconut sugar (if you want it to be sweeter, use regular sugar)

2 eggs, room temperature

1 tsp vanilla extract

Zest from one small lemon

1 ¾ cup gluten-free flour blend

¼ tsp salt

2 tsp baking powder

½ cup dairy-free milk

1 ½ cups blueberries, fresh or frozen

2 tbsp poppy seeds

2 tbsp sesame seeds

2 tbsp sunflower seeds

PREPARAZIONE

1. Preheat the oven to 350°F. Line a muffin tin with papers. Set aside.

2. In a large mixing bowl, mix oil and sugar with an electric mixer.

3. Add eggs, one at a time, beating well after each addition.

4. Add vanilla and lemon zest and mix until combined.

5. In a separate medium mixing bowl, whisk the flour, salt, and baking powder.

6. Slowly add to the wet mixture, alternating with the dairy-free milk.

7. Fold in blueberries and poppy, sesame, and sunflower seeds.

8. Fill each paper liner about 2/3 full.

9. Bake for 30-35 minutes, or until the center is set.

10. Remove from the oven and let cool for 10 minutes before transferring to a wire rack to cool completely.

11. Store in a container for up to 4 days at room temperature.

BANANA CHOCOLATE
chip muffins

SERVINGS: 12

PREP TIME: 10 MINS

COOK TIME: 20 MINS

TOTAL TIME: 30 MINS

INGREDIENTI

1 ½ bananas, mashed

1 ¼ cup gluten-free flour mix

½ cup coconut sugar

⅓ cup soy milk (or your favorite milk alternative)

⅓ cup coconut oil, melted

½ cup vegan chocolate chips

1 tsp Vanilla extract

1 tsp apple cider vinegar

1 tsp baking powder

¼ tsp baking soda

Lemon zest

Pinch of salt

Powdered sugar for topping

NOTES
You can use Cream
Cheese Frosting
(p 207)

PREPARAZIONE

1. Preheat the oven to 375˚F. Prepare a 12 cup muffin pan with paper liners.

2. Start preparing your dry mix. In a bowl, combine flour mix, baking powder, lemon zest and a pinch of salt

3. In another bowl, combine the wet mix, bananas, coconut oil, soy milk, vanilla extract, and apple cider vinegar.

4. Mix with a hand mixer until everything is evenly combined.

5. Add sugar and baking soda to the wet mix. Mix well.

6. Combine the dry mix and the wet mix together and run the hand mixer until everything is evenly combined.

7. Add chocolate chips and mix with a spoon.

8. Divide the batter into the 12 muffin cups and bake for 18 minutes. Muffins are done when golden or when a toothpick is inserted in the middle and comes out clean. Continue checking every 2 minutes if additional time is needed. Let cool for about 5-10 minutes and enjoy them warm.

9. Sift powdered sugar on top, or if you prefer, top them with your favorite frosting.

199

LEMON POPPY
seed muffins

SERVINGS: 12

PREP TIME: 15 MINS

COOK TIME: 15 MINS

TOTAL TIME: 30 MINS

INGREDIENTI

2 cups gluten-free all-purpose flour (with xanthan gum included)

2 tbsp poppy seeds

2 tsp aluminum-free baking powder

¼ tsp baking soda

½ tsp fine sea salt

¼ cup granulated sugar

Zest from 1 medium lemon

1 medium lemon, juiced

3 eggs, room temperature

¼ tsp lemon essential oil *optional*

8 tbsp vegan butter

1 cup plain vegan yogurt

For the Glaze

1 cup powdered sugar

1 tbsp fresh lemon juice (about 1/2 a medium lemon, juiced)

Zest from 1 medium lemon

PREPARAZIONE

1. Preheat the oven to 400°F and line a 12 cup muffin tin with paper liners or spray with non-stick spray.

2. In a large bowl, place the flour, baking powder, baking soda, salt, ¾ cup granulated sugar, lemon zest, and poppy seeds, and whisk to combine well.

3. In a separate bowl, place the vegan butter, vegan yogurt, lemon juice, and eggs, then whisk until smooth and very well combined. Create a well in the center of the dry ingredients, and pour in the wet ingredients. Mix until just combined.

4. Transfer the batter to the 12 muffin cups, they will be almost filled.

5. Bake for 14-16 minutes or until the toothpick comes out dry. Do not over-bake. When done, remove from the baking pan immediately and cool completely on a wire rack. Cool before adding the glaze.

6. **For the Glaze.** Add the powdered sugar, fresh lemon juice, and lemon zest to a small bowl. Stir together until smooth. Drizzle over cooled muffins or use a spoon to cover the tops like a glaze.

PEANUT BUTTER
crunch bars

SERVINGS: 10 BALLS

PREP TIME: 5 MINS

REST TIME: 1 HR

TOTAL TIME: 45-50 MINS

You will need an 8x8 inch pan

INGREDIENTI

⅓ cup agave

½ cup peanut butter

¼ tsp sea salt

¼ tsp cinnamon

2 ½ cups puffed rice cereal

7 oz dark chocolate

PREPARAZIONE

1. Line an 8x8 inch pan with parchment paper.

2. Add agave, peanut butter, salt, and cinnamon to a bowl, and stir to combine.

3. Add the rice puffs to the bowl and stir until well-coated.

4. Spread the mixture in the pan and press it down firmly.

5. Melt dark chocolate in a double boiler or in the microwave and pour over the puff mixture.

6. Put it in the fridge for about 1 hour, or in the freezer for a shorter time.

7. Cut into bars and enjoy! Store in a container in the fridge.

VEGAN LEMON
fat bombs

SERVINGS: 10 BALLS

PREP TIME: 5 MINS

REST TIME: 40-45 MINS

TOTAL TIME: 45-50 MINS

INGREDIENTI

8 oz vegan cream cheese

¼ cup coconut oil, melted

⅓ cup coconut flour

1 tsp fresh lemon juice

1 tbsp of lemon zest

1 teaspoon vanilla extract, *optional

3 tsp maple syrup

1 cup fine shredded unsweetened coconut

PREPARAZIONE

1. Combine all ingredients, except the shredded coconut, into a bowl until a thick dough forms. Place in the freezer for 10 minutes.

2. In the meantime, sift shredded coconut. Remove the dough from the freezer. Form golf-sized balls with the dough and roll them into the shredded coconut.

3. Arrange on a baking sheet lined with parchment paper. Freeze for 30-45 minutes.

4. Enjoy immediately or store in the fridge, or freezer in an air-tight container!

VEGAN MERINGUE

SERVINGS: 15 MINS

REST TIME: 1 HR

COOK TIME: 45 MINS

TOTAL TIME: 2 HRS

INGREDIENTI

½ cup aquafaba liquid from a can of chickpeas

¼ tsp cream of tartar

½ cup white granulated sugar

½ tsp vanilla extract

PREPARAZIONE

1. Place the chickpea liquid (aquafaba) and cream of tartar into the bowl of your stand mixer.

2. Start at a slow speed and whip until foamy.

3. Then gradually increase speed until white and glossy and stiff peaks start to form.

4. Add the sugar slowly while whipping at a fast speed.

5. Add in the vanilla.

6. Keep whipping until glossy stiff peaks form.

7. Preheat your oven to 250°F.

8. Line a baking tray with parchment paper.

9. Pipe the meringue mix into cookie shapes onto the parchment-lined tray. Alternatively, you can spoon it out, but I find piping to be much easier.

10. Place into the oven and bake for 45 minutes. After 45 minutes, switch off the oven but DON'T OPEN IT! Excuse the caps, but this part is very important. Leave the oven off, but don't open it for 1 hour. Time it.

11. After the meringues have baked for 45 minutes and then sat in the oven for a further 60 minutes without opening the oven, remove them from the oven.

12. They should be airy, crispy perfection! If the weather is at all hot or humid, put them in an airtight container and store them in the fridge for 7 days.

CHOCOLATE LAYER CAKE WITH
cream cheese frosting

SERVINGS: 8

PREP TIME: 20 MINS

COOK TIME: 40 MINS

TOTAL TIME: 1 HR

You will need two 8 inch round cake pans

INGREDIENTI

1 cup coconut sugar

¼ cup cane sugar

2 cups all-purpose gluten-free flour blend

¾ cup cacao powder

1 ½ tsp gluten-free baking powder

1 ½ tsp baking soda

1 tsp salt

2 large eggs, room temperature

1 cup milk alternative

¾ cup avocado oil (or plant-based butter)

1 ½ tsp vanilla extract

For the Cream Cheese Frosting

½ cup unsalted Earth Balance butter, softened

1 (8 oz) package plant-based cream cheese, softened

1 tsp vanilla extract

3 cups powdered sugar, plus more as needed

PREPARAZIONE

1. Preheat the oven to 350°F. Position rack in center of oven. Grease two 8 inch round cake pans. Set aside.

2. In a large mixing bowl, stir together flour, cocoa, baking powder, baking soda, and salt until there are no visible clumps.

3. Add eggs, milk, oil, vanilla, and sugar in a separate bowl. Beat with a mixer on medium speed for two minutes.

4. Spoon batter evenly into cake pans. Bake for 35-38 minutes, or until a toothpick inserted in the center comes out clean.

5. Remove from the oven and let cool in the pan for 5 minutes, then remove from the pan and let cool on a rack.

For the frosting

1. Combine butter and cream cheese in the bowl of a stand mixer (or you may use an electric mixer) and beat until creamy, well-combined, and lump-free.

2. Add vanilla extract and salt and stir well to combine.

3. With the mixer on low, gradually add powdered sugar until completely combined.

4. Assemble and frost. If cooled cakes are domed on top, use a large serrated knife to slice a thin layer off the tops to create a flat surface. This is called "leveling" the cakes. Discard or crumble over the finished cake. Place 1 cake layer on your cake stand or serving plate. Evenly cover the top with frosting. Top with the 2nd layer and spread the remaining frosting all over the top and sides. I always use an icing spatula for the frosting. Garnish with chocolate chips, if desired.

LEMON TURMERIC
chia seed pudding

SERVINGS: 2

PREP TIME: 10 MINS

REST TIME: 1 HR

TOTAL TIME: 1 HR 10 MINS

INGREDIENTI

1 can of coconut milk

1 cup water

7 tbsp chia seeds

2 lemons, juiced

1 ½ tsp turmeric

Pinch of black pepper

Pinch of salt

5 tbsp maple syrup

½ tsp Cardamom

PREPARAZIONE

1. Add all the ingredients together and mix well.

2. Pour the mix into a glass jar or air-tight container and let it rest in the fridge for at least 1 hour, preferably overnight.

CHOCOLATE
chia seed pudding

SERVINGS: 4

PREP TIME: 10 MINS

REST TIME: 1 HR

TOTAL TIME: 1 HR 10 MINS

INGREDIENTI

2 cups of your favorite milk alternative

2 tbsp cacao powder

5 tbsp maple syrup

½ tsp ground cinnamon

1 pinch sea salt

½ tsp vanilla extract

7 tbsp chia seeds

PREPARAZIONE

1. Add all the ingredients together and mix well.

2. Pour the mix into a glass jar or air-tight containerer and let it rest in the fridge for at least 1 hour, preferably overnight.

Spirulina Protein Balls (p 214)

PB Chocolate Protein Balls (p 215)

Goji Berry Maca Protein Balls (p 213)

GOJI BERRY MACA
protein balls

SERVINGS: 10-15 BALLS

PREP TIME: 10 MINS

TOTAL TIME: 30 MINS

INGREDIENTI

4 oz macadamia nuts

½ cup almonds

½ cup pitted dates

1 tsp vanilla extract

1 tbsp coconut oil

1 tbsp maca powder

1 tbsp maple syrup

1 ½ tsp pumpkin spices

⅓ cup goji berries

Salt

⅓ cup coconut flakes

PREPARAZIONE

1. Put all ingredients except the coconut flakes in a food processor and pulse at a slow speed to begin with. The ingredients should start to clump together; once this happens, you can increase the speed to create a smooth paste.

2. Roll into 1 oz balls, and then roll the balls in the coconut flakes.

3. Store in an airtight container in the fridge.

SPIRULINA
protein balls

SERVINGS: 10-15 BALLS

PREP TIME: 10 MINS

TOTAL TIME: 30 MINS

INGREDIENTI

1 tbsp cacao nibs

1 cup dates, pitted

½ cup almonds

½ cup pumpkin seeds

1 tsp spirulina powder

2 tbsp chia seeds

1 tbsp brown rice protein powder *optional*

1 tsp coconut oil, melted

1 tbsp almond butter

¼ tsp cardamom powder

¼ tsp cinnamon powder Pinch salt

PREPARAZIONE

1. Add ingredients to the food processor and process until broken down. The mixture should stick together when pressed between fingers. Add 1-2 tbsp water if the mixture is too dry and process again.

2. Take away approx 2 tbsp of the mixture and press and roll into a ball with your hands. Repeat until the mixture is completely used. Roll some of the balls in extra cacao and/or coconut, if desired.

3. Refrigerate for at least 30 minutes before eating.

PB CHOCOLATE
protein balls

SERVINGS: 10-15 BALLS

PREP TIME: 5 MINS

TOTAL TIME: 30 MINS

INGREDIENTI

1 cup oats

½ cup of dates, pitted

⅓ cup peanut butter

3 tbsp coconut oil

2 tbsp cacao powder

1 tsp chia seeds

¼ tsp salt

1 tsp vanilla extract

¼ cup coconut flakes

¼ cup raw cashew nuts

PREPARAZIONE

1. Add ingredients to the food processor and process until broken down. The mixture should stick together when pressed between fingers. If the mixture is crumbling, add a couple more dates, and/or 1-2 tbsp of water and process again.

2. Spoon out approx 2 tbsp of the mixture and press and roll into a ball with your hands. Repeat until the mixture is completely used. Roll some of the balls in extra cacao and/or coconut, if desired.

3. Refrigerate for at least 30 minutes before eating.

VANILLA RAW
cheesecake

You will need a 9 inch nonstick spring pan

SERVINGS: 10

PREP TIME: 30 MINS

REST TIME: 3 HRS

TOTAL TIME:
3 HR 30 MINS

INGREDIENTI

4 cups raw cashew nuts, soaked

½ cup maple syrup

1 can coconut cream

4 tbsp coconut oil

1 tbsp vanilla extract

Pie Crust

½ cup pecans

½ cup almonds

½ cup dates, pitted

1 tbsp coconut oil

½ tsp cinnamon

½ tsp cardamom

PREPARAZIONE

Pie Crust

1. Place crust ingredients in your food processor and blend until smooth. Cover a 9 inch nonstick spring pan with plastic wrap.

2. Transfer mix to a pie spring pan and press the dough until it is evenly distributed.

Cheesecake Filling

1. Soak raw cashews for at least 1 hour. Drain, rinse and set aside.

2. Put all ingredients except cashews in a Vitamix or high-speed blender and blend well.

3. Add cashews last, and blend until smooth and creamy.

4. Pour the mix into the pie crust, level it, and freeze it for at least 3 hours.

5. When serving it, make sure you pull it out of the freezer and remove the plastic wrap from the bottom. Plate the cheesecake on a serving plate and top it with your favorite toppings. Store it in the fridge for a maximum of 7 days.

AVOCADO CHOCOLATE
mousse

SERVINGS: 8

PREP TIME: 10 MINS

REST TIME: 3 HRS

TOTAL TIME:
1 HR 10 MINS

You will need a 9 inch nonstick spring pan

INGREDIENTI

4 large avocados

¾ cup of cacao powder

¾ cup of maple syrup (or agave if sweeter)

1 tsp vanilla extract

4 tbsp coconut oil

Pinch of pink Himalayan sea salt

Pie Crust

½ cup pecans

½ cup almonds

½ cup dates, pitted

1 tbsp coconut oil

½ tsp cinnamon

½ tsp cardamom

Notes

If you are using small-medium avocados then you may add one more avocado for a total of 5 avocados unless you like it super chocolaty!

You can top it with your favorite toppings and make it into small portions by pouring the mixture into individual serving bowls or ramekins with or without crust (your choice).

PREPARAZIONE

Pie Crust

1. Place crust ingredients in your food processor and blend until smooth. Cover a 9 inch nonstick spring pan with plastic wrap. Transfer mix to a pie spring pan and press the dough until it is evenly distributed.

2. Store in a container for up to 4 days at room temperature.

Chocolate Filling

1. Cut open your avocado, remove the pits and spoon the avocado into the bowl of a food processor.

2. Pulse for 1 minute or so, just to break them up a bit.

3. Then add in the rest of the ingredients. Pulse for 2 minutes, or until well combined.

4. Pour the mix into the pie crust, level it, and freeze it for at least 3 hours.

5. When serving it, make sure you pull it out of the freezer and remove the plastic wrap from the bottom. Plate mousse on a serving plate and top it with your favorite toppings. Store it in the fridge for a maximum of 7 days.

Breakfast, Smoothies
ELIXIRS

TOFU SCRAMBLE

SERVINGS: 2

PREP TIME: 5 MINS

COOK TIME: 15 MINS

TOTAL TIME: 20 MINS

INGREDIENTI

1 block organic soft tofu, drained

A handful of spinach or arugula

2 roma tomatoes, diced

1 cup mushrooms, chopped

½ small yellow onion, chopped

1 tsp ground cumin

1 tsp turmeric powder

¼ tsp garlic powder

½ tsp chili powder

2 tbsp nutritional yeast

1 garlic clove, minced

½ tsp salt

2 tbsp extra virgin olive oil

PREPARAZIONE

1. Add spices and tofu to a bowl. With clean hands, mix together until evenly combined.

2. Heat a skillet over medium heat and pour the extra virgin olive oil in.

3. Add the mushrooms, yellow onion, and garlic and saute for about 5 minutes.

4. Add tofu mixture to the skillet. Continue to cook, stirring occasionally, until the tofu is hot and extra liquid has evaporated so it looks like scrambled eggs.

5. Add roma tomatoes and spinach or arugula. Stir for 1 minute. Serve.

AVOCADO EGG
toast

SERVINGS: 1

PREP TIME: 5 MINS

COOK TIME: 3-5 MINS

TOTAL TIME: 10 MINS

INGREDIENTI

1 slice gluten-free bread, toasted

½ avocado, mashed

cooking spray

1 large egg

Kosher salt and black pepper to taste

Hot sauce, *optional

PREPARAZIONE

1. Mash the avocado in a small bowl and season with salt and pepper.

2. Heat a small nonstick skillet over low heat, spray with oil and gently crack the egg into the skillet. Cover and cook to your liking.

3. Place mashed avocado over toast. Top with egg, salt, pepper, and hot sauce, if desired!

NOTES
If you do not feel like having the egg on top of avocado toast, follow the steps and skip the egg!

EGG MUFFINS

SERVINGS: 12

PREP TIME: 10 MINS

COOK TIME: 15-20 MINS

TOTAL TIME: 25-30 MINS

INGREDIENTI

10 large eggs

1 tsp salt

¼ tsp black pepper

1 cup almond milk (or milk alternative of choice)

For the broccoli

1 ½ cups broccoli florets, finely chopped

¼ cup almond cheese, diced

For the spinach and sun-dried tomato

¼ cup sun-dried tomatoes, finely chopped

1 cup fresh baby spinach, chopped

¼ cup diced almond cheese

Notes:

Store leftover egg muffins in an airtight container or zip top bag in the refrigerator for up to 3 days, or individually wrap and freeze for up to 3 months.

PREPARAZIONE

1. Preheat the oven to 375°F. Coat 12 cups of a muffin tin with cooking spray or line with paper liners.

2. Crack the eggs into a large bowl. Use a hand blender or a whisk to blend the eggs until smooth, this will take less than 1 minute.

3. Fill the 12 muffin cups with your fillings of choice. I like to make 6 of each variation and fill the cups as much as I evenly can.

4. Divide the egg mixture evenly among the muffin cups.

5. Bake for 15-18 minutes or until eggs are set.

OATMEAL

SERVINGS: 1

PREP TIME: 2 MINS

COOK TIME: 3-5 MINS

TOTAL TIME: 5-7 MINS

INGREDIENTI

½ cup rolled oats

1 cup milk alternative (any kind) or water

Optional add-ins:

1 small banana, or preferred fruit

¼ cup pecans, chopped

½ tsp ground cinnamon

½-1 tbsp maple syrup

1 tsp ghee or coconut oil, if desired

PREPARAZIONE

1. Place ½ cup rolled oats and 1 cup liquid into a medium pot.

2. Bring to a boil over high heat while continuously stirring. Then, reduce heat to low and continue to stir for around 3-5 minutes, or until oats have thickened. Add more liquid if necessary.

3. Top it with your favorite toppings.

BERRY CHIA
yogurt parfait

SERVINGS: 1

PREP TIME: 5 MINS

TOTAL TIME: 5 MINS

Use an 8 oz mason jar.

INGREDIENTI

1 cup yogurt, dairy free

¼ cup gluten-free granola

Fresh fruit, berries

1 tsp of chia seeds

1 tsp of hemp seeds

PREPARAZIONE

1. Fill each jar with yogurt.

2. Top with granola.

3. Finish with a layer of fresh fruit, chia seeds, and hemp seeds.

4. Eat it right away or pop a lid on the jar and store it in the refrigerator for up to 3-4 days, depending on the ripeness of your fruit.

WAFFLES

SERVINGS: 3

PREP TIME: 10 MINS

REST TIME: 10 MINS

COOK TIME: 10 MINS

TOTAL TIME: 30 MINS

INGREDIENTI

1 ½ cup gluten-free flour mix (with xantham gum included)

1 ½ tsp baking powder

¼ tsp salt

Pinch of cinnamon *optional

¾ cup room temperature milk alternative of choice

¼ cup coconut or avocado oil, melted

2 eggs

1 tbsp maple syrup

1 tsp vanilla extract

PREPARAZIONE

1. In a bowl, whip 2 egg whites until stiff. Set aside.

2. In a mixing bowl, whisk together the dry ingredients: flour mix, baking powder, salt, and cinnamon. In another bowl, whisk together the wet ingredients: dairy-free milk, melted coconut oil or avocado oil, egg yolks, maple syrup, and vanilla extract.

3. Pour the wet ingredients into the dry ingredients. Stir with a big spoon until just combined (the batter will still be a little lumpy). By hand, fold it gently into egg whites. Let the batter rest for 10 minutes, so the flour has time to soak up some of the moisture. Plug in your waffle iron to preheat now (if your waffle iron has a temperature/browning dial, set it to medium-high).

4. Once 10 minutes is up, give the batter one more swirl with your spoon. Pour batter onto the heated waffle iron, enough to cover the center and most of the central surface area, and close the lid. Once the waffle is deeply golden and crisp, transfer it to a cooling rack or baking sheet. Don't stack your waffles on top of each other, or they'll lose crispness.

5. Repeat with the remaining batter. Serve waffles with maple syrup, plant-based butter, berries, or any other toppings that sound good!

PANCAKES

SERVINGS: 8-10

PREP TIME: 5 MINS

COOK TIME: 15 MINS

TOTAL TIME: 20 MINS

INGREDIENTI

1 ¼ cup gluten-free flour*

2 tsp baking powder

½ tsp salt

3 tbsp plant-based butter

1 ¼ cup milk alternative

1 egg

1 tbsp monk fruit sugar *optional

PREPARAZIONE

1. In a large bowl, sift together the flour, baking powder, salt, and sugar.

2. Make a well in the middle and pour in the milk alternative of choice, egg, and melted plant-based butter; mix with a fork or whisk until smooth.

3. Heat a non-stick pan over medium-high heat. Rub a small amount of plant-based butter or oil directly onto the pan.

4. Pour or scoop ¼ cup of batter for each pancake. Wait until bubbles form to flip. Brown on the other side and serve with plant-based butter, maple syrup, and your favorite toppings.

NOTES

I used Bob's Red Mill
1 to 1 Baking FLour.

Green Goddess Smoothie (p 231) | Strawberry Vanilla Smoothie (p 232)

PB Chocolate Smoothie (p 233) | Blueberry Smoothie (p 234)

Mango Ginger Turmeric Smoothie (p 235)

GREEN GODDESS
smoothie

SERVINGS: 1

PREP TIME: 5 MINS

BLEND TIME: 1 MINS

TOTAL TIME: 6 MINS

INGREDIENTI

1 banana, frozen

1 cup dairy-free milk of your choice

2 dates, pitted

½ green apple

⅓ avocado

1 cup spinach

1 tbsp chia seeds

½ tsp spirulina powder

PREPARAZIONE

1. Place the ingredients in a blender or Vitamix.
2. Blend until completely smooth.
3. Pour into a glass and serve.

STRAWBERRY VANILLA
smoothie

SERVINGS: 1

PREP TIME: 5 MINS

BLEND TIME: 1 MINS

TOTAL TIME: 6 MINS

INGREDIENTI

1 banana (preferably room temperature)

½ cup strawberries, froze*

½ cup non-dairy yogurt

½ cup non-dairy milk

2 dates, pitted

1 tsp vanilla extract

1 scoop of collagen or your favorite protein powder, if desired

PREPARAZIONE

1. Place the ingredients in a blender or Vitamix.

2. Blend until completely smooth.

3. Pour into a glass and serve.

PB CHOCOLATE
smoothie

SERVINGS: 1

PREP TIME: 5 MINS

BLEND TIME: 1 MINS

TOTAL TIME: 6 MINS

INGREDIENTI

1 frozen banana

1 cup dairy-free milk of your choice

2 tbsp peanut butter

2 dates, pitted

1-2 tablespoons cacao powder (or use unsweetened cocoa powder)

1 tsp vanilla extract

1 scoop collagen or your favorite protein powder, if desired

PREPARAZIONE

1. Place the ingredients in a blender or Vitamix.

2. Blend until completely smooth.

3. Pour into a glass and serve, topped with cacao nibs, if desired.

BLUEBERRY
smoothie

SERVINGS: 1

PREP TIME: 5 MINS

BLEND TIME: 1 MINS

TOTAL TIME: 6 MINS

INGREDIENTI

1 banana

½ cup blueberries, frozen

1 cup dairy-free milk of your choice

2 dates, pitted

½ tsp cinnamon

1 tbsp of chia seeds

¼ tsp cardamom

1 scoop collagen or your favorite protein powder, if desired

PREPARAZIONE

1. Place the ingredients in a blender or Vitamix.

2. Blend until completely smooth.

3. Pour into a glass and serve, topped with blueberries and mint, if desired.

MANGO GINGER
turmeric smoothie

SERVINGS: 1

PREP TIME: 5 MINS

BLEND TIME: 1 MINS

TOTAL TIME: 6 MINS

INGREDIENTI

1 banana, preferably room temperature

1 cup mango, frozen

1 cup dairy-free milk of your choice

2 dates, pitted

½ tsp turmeric

½ tsp dry ginger

1 scoop collagen or your favorite protein powder, if desired

PREPARAZIONE

1. Place the ingredients in a blender or Vitamix.

2. Blend until completely smooth.

3. Pour into a glass and serve.

Chai Latte (p 238)

Golden Turmeric Milk Latte (p 237)

GOLDEN TURMERIC
milk latte

SERVINGS: 1

PREP TIME: 3 MINS

COOK TIME: 2 MINS

TOTAL TIME: 5 MINS

INGREDIENTI

1 cup dairy-free milk of your choice

½ tsp turmeric

¼ tsp coconut oil

⅛ tsp pumpkin spices *optional*

1-2 tsp maple syrup or honey (that's just my preference but you can add more)

PREPARAZIONE

1. In a small saucepan over low-medium heat, whisk together milk, coconut oil, and spices. Cook, frequently stirring, until warm but not boiling.

2. Remove the saucepan from heat and let it cool for about 2 minutes.

3. Add your sweetener, and enjoy!

CHAI LATTE

SERVINGS: 1

PREP TIME: 5 MINS

COOK TIME: 5 MINS

TOTAL TIME:
10 MINS

INGREDIENTI

1 cup water

½ cup almond milk (or milk alternative of choice)

¼ tsp cinnamon powder

2 whole cloves

¼ tsp ground cardamom

1 star anise

¼ tsp ginger powder

1 tbsp maple syrup or honey

PREPARAZIONE

1. Place all ingredients, except the milk, in a saucepan on medium heat. Bring to a boil and stir in spices until they are well dissolved.

2. Boil until water is reduced by about half the volume.

3. Add in almond milk and lower heat to low-medium. Continue to cook for 2-3 minutes longer.

4. Remove from heat and strain. Add maple syrup or honey and enjoy.

HOT CHOCOLATE
Italian-style

SERVINGS: 3

PREP TIME: 10 MINS

SOAKING TIME: 1 HOUR

COOK TIME: 3-5 MINS

TOTAL TIME:
1 HR 10 MINS

INGREDIENTI

1 cup cashew nuts, soaked

3 cups water

⅓ cup cacao powder

⅓ cup maple syrup

1 tsp vanilla extract

Pinch of pink Himalayan sea salt

Pinch of cayenne or cinnamon *optional

PREPARAZIONE

1. Soak 1 cup of cashew nuts in a bowl of hot water, cover and let soak for a minimum of 1 hour.

2. Drain, then place the soaked cashews in a high-speed blender along with 3 cups of water. Blend on high for about 1 minute until smooth.

3. Add cacao powder, vanilla extract, a pinch of pink Himalayan sea salt, and maple syrup. Blend again for a few seconds, until evenly combined.

4. If you don't have a high-speed blender, strain the cashew milk through a fine mesh strainer or some cheesecloth to remove the cashew pulp.

5. To prepare 1 serving of Homemade Hot Chocolate, start by heating up 1 cup of the mixture in a small saucepan over medium-high heat.

6. Continue whisking the mixture until it comes to a boil. Boil for 1-3 minutes until it thickens a little.

7. Pour it into your favorite mug and enjoy!

TRIDOSHIC TEA

Let's take a look at each ingredient for this Ayurvedic tea recipe:

Cumin is specifically good for Kapha. **Cumin is wonderful for kindling the digestive fire.** It is hot in potency, so it's good for Kapha, which is heavy and damp. It's drawing up and clearing the channels and igniting that inner fire. It's also good for prevention of things like diarrhea, for people who tend to have loose motion.

Coriander seeds are the seeds of a plant you might know very well as cilantro. It has a cooling potency. It is very good for the fiery Pitta. **Coriander is wonderful for calming down inflammation and calming down the acidic feeling in the stomach and the small intestine.** It also can bring alkalinization into your whole system.

Fennel is the sweetest of the three and is especially good for a Vata dosha. **Fennel is wonderful for countering bloating** and wonderful for symptoms like IBS, and irritable bowel syndrome. It also moves the lymph and is a wonderful detoxifying agent.

INGREDIENTI

1 tsp cumin seeds

1 tsp coriander seeds

1 tsp fennel seeds

4 cups of water

PREPARAZIONE

1. In a small pan over high heat, bring water to a boil. Turn off the heat.

2. Add coriander, cumin, and fennel seeds and let steep for at least 5 minutes.

3. Strain and serve the desired amount. Store it in the fridge for up to 3 days.

About THE AUTHOR

Sara Garofalo is an Author, Certified Intuitive Health and Life Coach, Energy Healer, and Ayurveda Counselor. Sara helps unleash your own healing power through food, pleasure, and self-love.

Sara's work is based on the belief that all humans are innately intuitive. Her food, recipes, intuitive healing sessions, and coaching programs serve as a vessel to connect people back to their God-given gifts.

Sara lives in San Luis Obispo, California, with her two young children and enjoys spending her weekend by the beach or in nature, where she can connect with her soul.

Connect with her on Instagram @love.holistic.living and download her free ultimate guide to spiritual weight loss.

Reach out to Sara on her website: http://www.loveholisticliving.com/

ACKNOWLEDGEMENTS

I have immense gratitude for my Italian family and community who supported me through the entire process and showed up for me when I needed them most.

Thank you to my North American friends and community who supported me in bringing this book to life with editing, loving kindness, and honest opinions.

Thank you to all the hands that played a role in the creation of this book—from the Exalted Publishing House Team to the lifestyle photographer who captured the essence of my soul and the Universe for aligning everything perfectly for me to continue spreading healing and raising consciousness.

Publisher: Exalted Publishing House

Editor: Carly Ferguson + Rachel Oster

Book Design: Sara Garofalo + Exalted Publishing House Team

Lifestyle photographer: Svetlana Cozlitina

Food photographer: Sara Garofalo

Project Manager: Kristina Brummer

Location: Al Dossello

Via per Monterotondo, 24, 25050 Provaglio d'Iseo BS, Italy

ISBN: 978-1-7371857-9-6

Email: publishing@bridgetaileen.com

Disclaimer:

This publication contains the opinions and ideas of its author(s). It is intended to provide helpful and informative material on the subject matter covered. It is sold with the understanding that the author(s) and publisher are not engaged in rendering professional services in the book. If the reader requires personal assistance or advice, a competent professional should be consulted. The author(s) and publisher specifically disclaim any responsibility for any liability, loss, or risk, personal or otherwise, which is incurred as a consequence, directly or indirectly, of the use and application of any contents of this book.

Buon appetito!
Con amore,

Sara

LOVE
HOLISTIC LIVING

Made in the USA
Las Vegas, NV
22 November 2023

81341635R00148